W9-CCS-225

Clint Arthur's

9
FREE
SECRETS
OF
NEW
SENSUAL
POWER

This entertaining true story will guide you to
Professional, Personal & Spiritual Success
using simple systems for Sexual Ecstasy.

A SIGNATURE LOVE BOOK

PUBLISHED BY NEW SEX INSTITUTE
P.O. BOX 11682, MARINA DEL REY, CA 90295

SIGNATURE LOVE BOOKS
NEW SEX INSTITUTE
P.O. BOX 11682, MARINA DEL REY, CA 90295

http://www.NewSensualPower.com

Library of Congress Cataloging-in-Publication Data
Arthur, Clint
9 Free Secrets of New Sensual Power:
A true story that guides you to Personal, Professional, and
Spiritual Success through simple systems for Sexual Ecstasy /
Clint Arthur.

Originally published: Los Angeles :
Signature Love Books, © 2002
1.   Success – Sensual aspects. I. Title.

ISBN 0-9701637-8-9

ACKNOWLEDGMENTS

I would like to thank the following men
and women for their support,
encouragement, and inspiration:

Paul Roth, Justin Sterling, Tony Robbins, Frank McCourt,
Jim Rohn, Robert Kiyosaki, Miguel Ruiz, Tom Leonardi,
Mike Litman, Deepak Chopra, Madonna, Mel Gibson, Dr.
Corynna Clarke, Goddess Mare Simone, Goddess Natalia,
Goddess Laurel, Goddess Lilith, Jillian Speer, Tuesday,
Myles Bass, Mom, Dad, Chuckie-baby, Mimi & Glue,
Amazon.com, David Letterman, Oprah, Martha Stewart,
Emeril, David Andersen, Maharaji, Brian Ferrabee, Darin
Humecki, Tom Garcin, Joe McSpadden, Matt Davis,
Robert Fruchtbaum, Gabe Watson, Mitch Desser, Dr. Phil,
Willie Nelson, Mick Jagger, Bruce Springsteen, Billy Joel,
Denes Petoe, Mark Williams, Notorious BIG, Clifford,
Thomas J. Stanley, Al Reis, Zig Ziglar, John Barker Jr.,
Charlie Trotter, Matthias Merges, Allessandro Stratta, Jean-
Georges Vongrichten, Doc Lawrence, Herbert Hardesty,
Fellah, Doctor John, Christopher Barrett, Anne Schedeen,
John Favreau, Capt. Larry Schneider, Rodney Boothroyd,
Michael Ognibene, Cher, Stephen Leib, Goddess Suzie,
Sara Schedeen, Mini, Van Morrison, Dr. Stuart Glassman,
Dr. Sam Fager, Dr. Gary Schubach, Charles Muir, Wendy
Cooper, Mike Bertrand, Ron Meyer, Ed Powers, Aria
Giovanni, Ronald Reagan, Bill Clinton, Evan Sarver,
Anne & Arnold Kopelson, Sean Young, Nicholas Cage,
Norah Jones, Lester Barrie, Tom Cruise, Hoody,
Joe Vitale, Erik Rothenberg, Martin Hannon, Jeff Herman,
Charles Sherman, Pablo Picasso, Arthur T. Gates,
Clay Smith, Muddy Waters, Bill Gates, Steve Jobs,
and most importantly, Alison "Honey" Savitch.

This book is dedicated to all who desire
more success, power, money, sex,
intimacy, love, and fulfillment in life.

CONTENTS

INTRODUCTION

When I was twenty-seven years old, I was visiting my parents in the living room of their Midtown Manhattan apartment when they suddenly erupted into an argument. Dad stormed into their bedroom, slamming the door behind him.

After a few seconds of silence I looked at my mom and said, "The way he resents you – it seems like you've been having affairs. Is that why you two are always fighting – because you've been having affairs?"

She didn't say anything for a few seconds.

Just sat there.

I saw her jugular vein pulse with blood four times.

Then she looked at the closed bedroom door with sadness and resentment plain in her features, and said, "He just doesn't know how to do me."

Shortly thereafter, my parents' traditional values wore out, and they divorced after nearly four decades of screaming at each other.

Although I didn't realize it until I sat down to write this book, from the moment of that conversation onward, my life was guided by a new purpose: to make sure that my marriage would <u>never</u> be destroyed because I didn't know how to "do" my wife the way she needed to be done.

In all fairness to Dad and Mom, my parents were victims of their day and age. Their generation thought that sexual performance was a NATURAL skill, one which you either had or didn't have. It never occurred to them that they could <u>seek out knowledge and expertise to become great lovers.</u>

Much to my benefit, they always emphasized the importance of education. As a result, I have learned how to take most any woman to realms of sexual pleasure beyond what most people ever experience. And by harnessing that powerful force of nature, can share the height of ecstasy with a sexual partner each and any time I try. But great sex is just the tip of the iceberg.

Surprisingly, one of the great results of my nine-year quest has been the realization that sexual mastery is not only the foundation of great spousal relationships, but can also be the most potent source of power for every other type of interpersonal relationship, including those with one's friends and extended family, and even with clients, co-workers, and the public-at-large.

I have gone on to discover that sexual energy has been the secret force behind many of the world's superpowerful people, including United States presidents, titans of industry, and icons of popular culture.

In my own life, by using the lessons contained in this book my monthly income has gone from $1600 to $16,000 in less than two years. And I went from being celibate and alone, to being in love and in a committed long-term relationship with the most beautiful, intelligent, sexually compatible woman of my dreams. Our relationship has a bedrock foundation of intimacy that can only come from moments of shared mutual ecstasy and sexual wildness between a man and a woman.

On a metaphysical level, with Sacred Sexuality and Sex Magic, I have been able to manifest significant dreams, and most important, to bring into my life a personal understanding of, and relationship with, God.

The mission to expand my sexual knowledge included extensive research into the wisdom of ancient masters, cutting-edge modern methods, antique texts, contemporary anecdotes, surfing the furthest waves of the Internet, and personal experiences with internationally renowned sex experts.

In this book I will share with you all the intimate details of my journey from sexual naiveté to enlightenment at the altar of the Great Goddess Temple.

Along the way you will gain all the knowledge I accumulated in the process of writing *Ultimate Female Orgasms* (Simon & Schuster, UK) and by creating New Sex Institute's audio programs *Master Sex Talk* and *New Free Sex Oral* and instructional films *New Sex Now, Goddess Worship*, and *New Free Sex*™. I've also included the best *New Sex Advisor* columns I've written for my six million RiskyMail & TeenMail readers – as little breaks from the "main story."

For those of you with a family and children, I believe that the most important thing you can do for your children is master the lessons of this book, as the health and safety of children depends on a strong relationship between parents.

Many people believe that the quality of your life is determined by the quality of your communications. One of the most powerful and effective ways that men and women communicate is through sexual intercourse. By improving the quality of your sexual communication you will improve the quality of your overall communication with your significant other. This will have a spill-over effect that will improve every aspect of your life.

My solemn promise to you is to deliver everything I've got, in the fewest possible words, and to assure you that every secret you read about in this book can be used by you as much as you want with ABSOLUTELY NO FEES or ASSOCIATED COSTS. The Most Potent Powers on Earth will be at your unlimited disposal for FREE!

Wise students of this material will use these powers to accelerate the fruition of dreams and aspirations, and to enrich personal and professional relationships alike.

Sincerely,

Clint Arthur

How to Get the Most Out of This Book

The lessons of this book are presented to you in story form. In order to have the full benefit of my 9-year intensive quest for sexual mastery, all you have to do is read the story. As you become familiar with the step-by-step systems detailed in the text, you are advised to pay very close attention to the subtle distinctions that will lead to greater expertise and wrote mastery of the advanced sexual techniques and theories. By completing the Review Quizzes at the end of each chapter, you will qualify for accreditation by the New Sex Institute.

Enjoy, and good luck!

CA

1
HER ULTIMATE PLEASURE

A PHONE CALL & A FUNERAL

Soon after returning from New York and learning the deep, dark secret of my true genetic heritage, I was standing in the living room of my Venice Beach apartment, getting ready for a sunset surf session in the Pacific Ocean, when I received a phone call that was to play a key note in my destiny.

"Clint!" said the excited male voice on the other end of the line. "It's Leo!"

I had met Tommy Leonardi the very first day of freshman year at Stuyvesant High School. We wrestled on our school's Public School Athletic League Champion team (beating out the toughest juvenile delinquents from Brooklyn, Queens, Staten Island, and the Bronx), both went on to gain early acceptance into the Ivy League University of Pennsylvania, and became fraternity brothers in the coolest house on campus.

While living in the Castle during our sophomore year in college, Tommy and I spent many late nights discussing our (and especially his) varied and extensive sexual exploits with women. And after college, he would periodically call to fill me in on his latest *ménage-à-trois* or sex-toy discovery.

After ten years of talking about women, Tommy had absolutely no need to impress me. I knew what a total stud he was. The guy was a living legend in our fraternity and throughout the city of Philadelphia, where he lived.

In fact, when *Philadelphia* magazine circulated a sex survey asking, "In which of the following ten public places have you had sex?," Tommy checked off all ten and wrote in five more of his own—"under the bleachers in JFK Stadium," "in the Art Museum," "on the fifty-yard line of Franklin Field," and so on!

So when he said, "Dude, I'm doing this new thing to women, and it's driving them out of their frickin' minds!," I immediately perked up and asked, "New?"

"I'm telling you," he said with energy in his voice, "it's completely different from anything I've ever done before."

I sat down on the couch and asked, "So what is this new thing?"

He said, "I figured out how to give any woman female ejaculations."

I said, "What's a female ejaculation?"

He said, "When they cum, hot liquid explodes out of their vaginas."

"How much liquid?"

"Puddles in the bed. The sheets are completely soaked."

I asked, "And that's a good thing?"

He said, "I'm telling you, not only does it get the WOMEN more excited, but turning them on like that gets me hotter than anything I've experienced too. Dude, it's frickin' UNBELIEVABLE!"

His enthusiasm was contagious, and even though the Virgo in me was put off by the prospect of soiling my sheets with mysterious puddles of sexually excreted liquid, I asked, "Can you teach me how to do it?"

He said, "I guess so."

"How long would it take?"

"I don't know. I never taught it to anyone before. Maybe a couple hours, a couple days?"

At that point in my life I had already written fifteen feature film screenplays, and was a very fast writer. Sensing that this might be some kind of actual breakthrough sexual discovery, I asked, "Do you think we could write a book about it?"

He said, "I don't know."

Tommy agreed to think about his new technique and prepare to explain it to me, and we each agreed to try and figure out a place where we could get together to collaborate on a book, which I would write based on his techniques.

Soon thereafter, I received another phone call that would prove to be a monumental moment in my life, and the second note in the sexual symphony of my destiny: news that my grandfather had passed away.

I went back to New York for the funeral, and a few weeks later I flew back again to hang out with my bereaved grandmother at her house in Long Island. And so it came to pass that Tommy and I met and wrote our sex book during a three-day weekend at my sweet little granny's house on Long Island.

I remember just before I went to write the book, I was hanging out with one of our fraternity brothers, Evan Kopelson, and I told him I was going to write a book about Tommy's sex techniques and these new female orgasms.

He had never heard of female ejaculations either, and when I related the tiny bit of information Tommy had told me about them he said, "Whoa, I want to read that book!" The he looked at me very seriously and asked, "Does he do something with his nose?"

I said, "I don't know. But if he does, it will definitely be in the book."

For three solid days, I asked Tommy every possible question I could think of about his methods for having great sex and how to give any woman what he called Ultimate Female Orgasms.

"Then what do you do?" I asked him. "And then what happens? . . . And then what?"

Finally it got to the point where Tommy Leonardi said, "Dude, I have nothing left to say." If you knew Tommy Leonardi, you'd know that this was akin to someone draining off the entire flow of water at Niagara Falls.

He went for a walk around the block, and as I sat there at my grandmother's dining room table, she came in and sat down opposite me. "So this book your writing with your friend Tommy – what is he, some kind of sex expert?"

I said, "Well, Granny, you see, he knows how to give women very wet orgasms."

She said, "Oh, I have those!"

Shocked, I said, "You do?"

She nodded. "My first husband, Leon Wanger – we were making love one day in 1926, and he said to me, 'Baby, you've gotta let go!' So I did."

That was basically what Tommy had been explaining to me for three days! How to make women "let go."

He had even played microcassette tapes of interviews he had conducted with women who had experienced these new orgasms with him using his technique. They had specifically said, "You have to let go and go over a wall to this new kind of pleasure."

Many of them had said that this was "different" and "much more intense" than "regular orgasms."

And that these ejaculatory climaxes "are the Ultimate Female Orgasms."

At that moment it became crystal clear to me that what was old had indeed become new again.

PHIL & SCRUMFY

I flew back to L.A. with the completed manuscript detailing Tommy Leonardi's techniques – and no, there was no mention of using his nose – printed it up on my personal LaserWriter, and gave a copy to one of my roommates, Phil.

Phil was a mild-mannered psychology student who was in a long-term relationship with a nice Jewish girl from Beverly Hills whom he affectionately referred to as Scrumfy. He wore black plastic glasses, played lots of computer games, and was pretty much a classic geek who would go on to make millions building websites during the early days of the Internet revolution. His girlfriend was quiet and shy, and taught kindergarten at an Orthodox Jewish Hebrew School.

So Phil and Scrumfy went to Las Vegas that weekend for the Grateful Dead shows, and during the drive through the desert Phil mentioned that he had read my new book and wanted to try out some new sex techniques with her.

This was straight out of the book. <u>You discuss the idea of new sexual techniques with your lover while you're driving to Las Vegas, or when you're out to dinner, or while you're taking a walk on the beach.</u> BUT NEVER IN BED.

On Monday afternoon Phil came bursting through the front door of our apartment, more energized than I had ever seen him.

"It fuckin' worked!" he shouted. "She was squirting all over the place! All down her leg, all down my arm, all over the bed – it was fucking unbelievable!"

I looked at him wide-eyed. "Scrumfy?"

Nodding eagerly, he continued. "She was screaming and moaning – she's never been so wild in bed! It was amazing, dude. Thank you! And tell Tommy 'Thank you' for us both."

Phil's confirmation of the effectiveness of the techniques was a great thing. There was only one problem: I didn't have a girlfriend.

Here I was with the secrets of how to have a NEW SEX EXPERIENCE that transforms mild-mannered Jewish kindergarten teachers into screaming, squirting, sexual wild women – and I had no one to try it with!

EARTHQUAKE!

The following January was the big earthquake in L.A.

My mother called me the next day, worried half out of her mind. I told her I was unharmed, and she insisted, "I did the astrological projections, and you have to get out of that city right away – the entire West Coast is gonna fall into the sea!"

She had been right about some very extreme predictions in the past. She had once predicted that her friend's husband was going to die at a young age despite the fact that he was in perfect health and played competitive tennis three times a week. The guy dropped dead of a heart attack on a tennis court at the age of forty-nine.

So I asked, "Is Utah far enough away?"

She said, "That should be okay."

So I booked a ticket on Southwest Airlines, packed my long underwear, and jetted off to the Sundance Film Festival.

If you've never been to Sundance, here's how it works: All the big executives get to drive around in brand new SUVs that they rent with their fat-cat corporate expense accounts, and all the starving aspiring filmmakers, writers, and actors get to use the free buses to shuttle back and forth between snowed-in movie theaters.

I was riding one of those free shuttles to see the new hip feature film *Naked in New York* when onto the bus walked a sweet-looking, beautiful young woman in a unique wool coat.

As she walked up the aisle of the bus, I smiled at her and said, "Great coat!"

She said, "Thank you, I manufacture these coats out of antique blankets," and proceeded to walk to the back of the bus and ignore me for the rest of the ride.

Outside the theater where they were showing *Naked in New York*, I ran into a literary agent I knew named Maryanne. She was waiting on line to get standby tickets for the show, and in order to curry favor with a high-powered agent who might some day give my career a boost, I gave her two passes that someone had given me.

After the movie I noticed Maryanne saying goodbye to the beautiful woman in the blanket coat. I walked up to her and said, "So how'd you like *Naked in New York*?"

She said, "I liked it. My friend got us free passes from a friend of hers."

I said, "I know. I gave the tickets to Maryanne."

She said, "You know Maryanne?"

I nodded and smiled at the obvious change in her approachability. I was now approved because I was the friend of a high-ranking agent who was a mutual friend. She stuck out her hand and said, "I'm Beth."

I said, "Nice to meet you, Beth. My name is Clint."

It just so happened that I wanted to see the exact same movie that she was off to next, so even though neither of us had tickets, we rode over there together on the bus. This time she sat beside me and chatted the whole way.

Turned out that her father and I shared the exact same birthday. She said, "My father was a saint of a man. I loved daddy more than anyone in the whole world."

I said, "I'm sure he was a very cool guy."

She told me about a book called *Golf in the Kingdom*, and I wrote the name of it down on the back of a business card that proclaimed her a Talent Manager. "I just do the coats as a sideline business for fun," she explained.

It just so happened that my friend Bob Hawke was tearing the tickets at the door of the movie we were going to see. He was on the Sundance selection committee and had actually championed the movie into the festival. Bob was a gay guy I'd met on another free shuttle bus, and in order to curry favor with a young filmmaker who might someday suck his dick, he let us into the sold-out movie for free.

It just so happened that there were only two seats left in the entire theater, so we sat down next to each other as the lights dimmed.

She took off her coat and allowed the funky loose collar of her sweater to fall down below her bare shoulder beside me, revealing several strands of antique gold beads about her lovely throat. Right at that moment I was already in love.

I took her to dinner at a fancy Italian restaurant.

She brought me along to a big party thrown by Miramax.

By some coincidence we were staying at the exact same condo complex, so I walked her home and she showed me pictures of her with her boyfriend at the church formal. He was a much older guy with gray hair.

And out of the blue, as I said good night in her doorway, she planted a big fat smooch right on my lips.

Maryanne walked up the hall right at that very moment and screamed, "What the FUCK is going on here?!"

Beth said, "Nothing!" and smiled like a Cheshire cat.

I just smiled.

The following week, back in L.A., I called Beth and mentioned that I had read and enjoyed *Golf in the Kingdom*.

She said, "You are good." Then she said, "We should have lunch sometime. What are you doing Tuesday night?"

I said, "Having lunch with you?"

She took me to a DGA screening of a movie starring her ex-client Danny Quinn. Anthony Quinn was there, and we shook his hand. George Wendt was there because his kid was in the movie too, and she said hello to him also.

After the movie she said, "Let's get some dinner. We could either go out or we could go back to my house for some home-made chicken soup."

We ate and talked in her living room until midnight. When she walked me out her front door, I noticed the brilliant full moon, so I stood behind her and ran a finger down her spine while we looked at it for some moments. Then she turned and grabbed hold of the protruding hard-on which was bulging in my crotch.

Shocked, I said, "Beth!"

And she said, "You were poking me with it!"

By the following week she and her boyfriend of six months had broken up. She mentioned that she was going to a funeral in Palm Springs, and I invited myself along. And then, lo and behold, there we were in a hotel room at the Days Inn.

More than anything else in the world, I wanted the techniques to work. Desire is a key element of being successful with this (or any) technique or self-help program. Personally, I find it to be one of the most important.

If you really want something bad enough, if there's a fire burning inside you to accomplish a goal – any goal – you WILL find a way.

If you MUST give a woman female ejaculations, if you MUST make her think of you as a sexual god, then you will.

MY FIRST FEMALE EJACULATION

I began by slowly undressing Beth and undressing myself at the same time, keeping the level of nudity even...

Removing her brown, yellow, and black silk blouse, I tossed it over the lampshade to create DIM, COLORED MOOD LIGHTING...

Then, when she was naked, I lowered her down to lie on her back in the BIG, COMFORTABLE BED.

Then I poured some MASSAGE LOTION into my cupped hand, and rubbed it between my palms to warm it up...

Then I began massaging her fingers and hands...

Sensually rubbing the skin and muscles of her forearms...

Up along her biceps and triceps...

All the while looking into her beautiful blue eyes...

Massaging into her shoulders...

Then up her neck...

Up behind her ears...

The base of her skull...

Into her scalp...

Kissing her LIPS while lovingly rubbing the back of her head

Kissing her EYELIDS…

Lightly breathing on and brushing her BROWS with my lips…

Making sure to touch and kiss her TEMPLES…

BEHIND HER EARS…

And EVERY POSSIBLE UNUSUAL PLACE ON HER HEAD (AND ON THE REST OF HER BODY).

When you PAY ATTENTION TO UNUSUAL PLACES on a person's body, when you touch them in unusual ways (using your lips, or your cheek, or other different combinations), it makes that person feel like you're paying very special attention to them.

PAYING VERY SPECIAL ATTENTION TO A PERSON MAKES THAT PERSON FEEL ADORED.

Everyone wants to feel adored.

Everyone wants to feel special.

If you give someone the special feeling of being adored, IT WILL MAKE HER LIKE YOU MORE…

It will soften her to you…

Melt her defenses…

Dissolve the walls and barriers…

It will make her feel like you care…

And if a person feels that you care about her, she will TRUST you, and that trust will grow as she surrenders to your adoration.

Slowly I massaged Beth's whole head with my fingers, lips, and eyes…

SMELLING THE FRAGRANCE OF HER HAIR AND SKIN…

Taking in everything about her with all my senses…

Then I continued by LICKING AND KISSING HER THROAT…

Her COLLARBONE…

Down along the sides of her breasts…

Making CIRCLES AROUND HER AREOLAS with my fingers…

Slowly and softly rubbing around the brown circles and hardening nipples…

Then I licked my fingertips and softly circled them on the tips of her nipples…

Rubbing around the top edges of the nipples until they hardened and firmed…

Licking the edges of one nipple tip…

Then the other…

While I CUPPED AND SUPPORTED HER BREASTS IN MY HANDS…

Slowly breathing on and descending upon the nipple with my mouth…

Taking the entire right nipple into my mouth and FEELING it with my tongue…

With my lips…

Discerning the individual nooks and crannies of the interior structure of the breast…

Picturing those nooks and crannies with my mind's eye…

Pushing her breasts toward each other with my hands…

KISSING BOTH NIPPLES AT THE SAME TIME…

Sucking on them both…

Licking them both…

FEELING them…

Adoring them for a long time…

Then continuing the massage with my hands rubbing softly down her ribs…

Licking and kissing along each rib below the skin…

Really exploring, touching, and noticing the BONES…

Getting to that primal level of physical structure…

Noticing the differences between the skin and the muscles of her body…

Breathing on her belly button…

Massaging and sucking HIPBONES...

Down to her thighs...

The large muscles of her upper legs...

Swooshing my hands over the skin of her inner thighs...

Breathing on her inner thighs...

Massaging the muscles of her legs with a little more pressure...

More "therapeutically"...

MAKING SURE TO AVOID HER VAGINA...

Then moving down to her shins and lower legs...

Rubbing warmed-up lotion into her skin...

Down to her feet and toes...

Into and around each and every toe...

THE BALLS OF HER TOES...

THE WEBS BETWEEN THE TOES...

The ARCH...

Heel...

Rubbing and massaging as slowly and softly and lovingly as I could...

Watching her watch me...

Watching her enjoying the sensations I was giving her...

Then I softly instructed her to "Turn over."

She rolled onto her stomach...

And I continued to massage and lick my way up the backs of her legs...

Across the sensitive CREASES BEHIND HER KNEES...

Into her thighs...

And into her buttocks.

BODY PARTS ARE INTERCONNECTED

The buttocks were a key place where I first put Tommy's concept of interconnected body parts to work. Even though the buttocks are a separate part of the body, the flesh of the buttocks is directly connected to the skin of her vaginal lips...

So as I squeezed and massaged Beth's buttocks, I made sure to look and ACTUALLY SEE the connection between the flesh of her buttocks and the vaginal lips…

Watched the stretch of the butt cheek tugging on the wet lips…

Moving the right lip by squeezing the right buttock…

Sliding the glistening pink surface up and down against the other lip which stood more or less stationary…

She was squirming and breathing hard…

Moving her hips up and down…

Then I squeezed her left buttock to move the left side of her vagina up and down…

Watching it…

Watching and feeling and responding to the effect this had on her…

My own breath coming quicker…

MATCHING the pace of hers…

Allowing myself to become aroused, while at the same time remaining in control…

Following the "script" of the Ultimate Erotic Massage…

Then I began to BREATHE AND LICK THE SMALL OF HER BACK…

Her lower SPINE…

Massaging up her back with my fingers…

Always warming the lotion between my palms before putting it against her flesh…

Rubbing and sensually squeezing her shoulders…

Giving her a lovely, luscious, and leisurely shoulder massage before…

Turning her over and lying down next to her on the bed…

KEY BODY LANGUAGE

I put my left arm around Beth's shoulder and kept it there for the rest of the "experience."

With my left arm around her shoulder…
Hugging her tight with that left arm…
Holding her in THE SAFETY OF MY EMBRACE…
Looking into her eyes…
Seeing the impact on her…

KEY SIGN OF HER RELAXATION
A very RELAXED HUG of her own…
Both of her arms encircling my torso, gently, in a most relaxed manner…
More than anything, just keeping me close to her…
In contact with her…

KEY SIGN OF HER AROUSAL
The SEXY, WAVELIKE MOTION OF HER HIPS…
Moving back and forth against my thighs…
Not exactly grinding so much as moving in a turned-on, wavelike motion…
I knew that it was…

ALMOST TIME FOR VAGINAL STIMULATION
But first I went for Tommy's "Secret Hot Spot" on a woman's body…

THE SECRET HOT SPOT
Right above the pubic hair, below the belly button…
I softly placed my right palm on this hot spot and gently massaged it for about a minute. He had cautioned me that any more time than that and it would grow too sensitive…
As I softly made circular motions on this area, Beth continued to move her hips in that sexy, wavelike motion…
And we continued to kiss…
Our tongues dancing softly…
Then I moved my palm down over her pubic mound to…

<u>Carefully cup her entire vagina with my palm…</u>

Holding my skin an inch or so above her vaginal lips…

Allowing her to feel the warmth of my flesh…

Maintaining the distance as her <u>hips writhed and surged</u> to make contact with my palm…

ENJOYING THE IMPACT ON HER…

Knowing that this was TEASING her in a way she'd probably never before been teased…

Making sure to…

STAY AWAY FROM HER CLITORIS!

Women are used to clitoral stimulation and orgasms, and any contact with her clitoris will get her going down that road. But that's not the destination we want to get to, and rather than confuse her with that type of arousal, it's best to steer wide and clear of the little love button that normally would be the focus of attention.

CUP THE VAGINA

After about a minute of cupping the vagina, I placed one finger on either side of her vaginal lips and began to LIGHTLY SPREAD THE LIPS of her vagina…

Slowly moving them open.

Beth's lips were not very fleshy or flappy, so I just moved them to an open position. Had they been fleshy flaps, I could have folded them open to flatten out on top of the skin surrounding her vagina.

Whether they actually *fold* is not the key, what's important is the *movement* of the lips…

Holding them open and stroking up and down…

<u>Using her natural juices and wetness now to lubricate</u> the exterior of her vaginal lips…

FIRST CONTACT

Hugging her deliberately, I gently slid one finger inside Beth's vagina…

Curling the finger up around the pubic bone…

And lightly placing it on the area of ridges and bumps on the front wall of her vaginal vault…

HOW THRILLING FOR IT TO FEEL EXACTLY THE WAY TOMMY SAID IT WOULD!

I touched what he preferred to call the "G-area," which was about the size of a quarter (and which could vary in size, either smaller or larger…)

And I used THE LIGHTEST POSSIBLE TOUCH…

Noticing how different it felt than all the other vaginal wall textures that I'd ever felt…

Vaginal walls are flat and smooth…

But the G-spot could almost be described as being like corduroy…

Or like the nap of industrial carpet…

Rubbing the fingerprint pad of my finger as softly as possible on the ridges of her G-spot…

Beginning with a gentle motion sliding up and down over the bumps…

Slowly and softly…

Awakening her long-dormant realm of ultra-pleasure…

DELIBERATELY GIVING HER A LITTLE EXTRA SQUEEZE AND HUG with my arm that was STILL AROUND HER SHOULDER as I made first contact with the G-spot…

After a while, changing the type of stimulation…

Gently PRESSING IN on the G-spot, THEN LETTING GO…

PULSING softly…

SOOOOO SOFTLY…

And lo and behold, the BUMPS AND RIDGES BEGAN TO GO SMOOTH AND FLATTEN OUT!

Much as a nipple can change texture, going from soft to hard, and vice versa, the G-spot was responding the same exact way…

She was breathing visibly harder…

Faster…

And so was I!

This WAS turning me on…

I was enjoying giving her pleasure…

The excitement naturally prompted me to use more pressure and speed in my movements…

And I started CIRCLING THE G-SPOT WITH MY FINGERTIP…

Then alternating periodically between the three basic motions…

Until I felt the bumps and ridges return…

Once again exhibiting the rough texture so different from the rest of the interior vaginal surfaces…

So I slowed way down and softened way up…

Letting her catch her breath during this brief respite…

Then, as I began to feel the bumps and ridges flatten out again, I once again built up the pressure and speed of my stimulation…

ALTERNATING BETWEEN THE MOTIONS of rubbing up and down, in and out, pressing, and circling…

Soon I began to feel slight CONTRACTIONS in the walls and muscles of her vagina, occurring about a minute apart.

At first sign of these contractions, I gave her an extra hug or squeeze, that body language cue to subtly, subconsciously let her know that she was progressing the way I wanted her to.

And I continued the cat-and-mouse game of making her bumps and ridges go away, then increasing the pressure and speed to get her more excited, and decreasing it again when the roughness returned to her G-area…

Until the contractions came closer and closer together…

Building in frequency and intensity…

To the point where they could no longer be described as contractions, but rather, CONVULSIONS of her entire vaginal and pelvic area…

Her hips were going wild, grinding and bucking back and forth, up and down…

I had to hold her tight with my arm around her shoulder…

And my right bicep was getting a great workout…

My single finger inside her lacked the strength and grip to stimulate her as forcefully as she seemed to need…

So I gave Beth an extra hug around her shoulder and INSERTED A SECOND FINGER INSIDE HER to stimulate the region of bumps and ridges…

She seemed to love the circling and the pressing more than the in and out "finger-fucking," so I gave her more of those movements…

As I found myself grinding and humping against her hip with my raging erection…

Found myself breathing hard…

Groaning and moaning NATURAL SOUNDS OF ANIMAL AROUSAL…

Masculine echoes of her feminine pleasure moans…

SUDDENLY HER ENTIRE VAGINA GOT EXTREMELY WET…

Tommy had referred to this as the "pre-ejaculatory flood-rush"…

The liquid was different from regular vaginal lubrication in that it suddenly flooded the entire interior of the vagina…

And it was MUCH WETTER than regular vaginal lubrication…

But this flood-rush DID NOT SQUIRT OUT OF HER…

It was truly amazing, because it was happening just as Tommy had said it would…

And when it did, I gave her an extra hug with MY LEFT ARM, WHICH WAS STILL AROUND HER SHOULDER…

Groaned in approval…

And kept doing EXACTLY WHAT I WAS DOING with my fingers inside her…

Maintaining the pressure and speed and rhythm…

Allowing her to work with it…

Hanging onto her with my hugs, holding her in my physical control…

Throwing my right leg over her right leg to maintain control of her lower body, not letting her get away or squirm away…

It was SO INTENSE…

She was groaning and making noises like a wildcat…

I was glad I had experience as a champion wrestler, because if not I may not have been able to keep control of her and of the situation…

"Yeah, baby! I've got you! I've got you!" I said in some supermanly voice I'd never uttered before…

"Ohhhhhhhhh! Ohhhhhhhhhhh!" She couldn't talk, she couldn't understand what was happening to her…

As her level of arousal built and built and built…

Her body arching and tensing with energy and power!

I said, "I'VE GOT YOU!"

"OhGODDDDDDDDDDDDDDDDDDAAAAAAAAAHHH HHHHHHHHHHHHHHHHHHHHHHH!" she screamed with the first gush of hot, wet liquid explosion coming from deep within her.

WOW! I thought, growling "Raarrrgh!!!" – continuing now on natural impulse…

Feeling the heat of liquid gushing into my palm…

The climax seemed to subside, so I pressed in harder for a while, concentrating my mental energies and intentions, and before long she was screaming again: "AhhhhGoddddddAhh!"

With another gushing hot, wet explosion...

This time MORE LIQUID squirting out of her...

The puddle spreading on the bed to where I could feel it with my knee...

My eyes wide in amazement at *the animalness of this previously sweet, wholesome, down-to-earth young woman*...

The hardness of my erection raging!

My fingers pressing and squeezing out a THIRD gush...

Her soul letting go with another long, primal "OHHHGODDDDDAAAAAHHHH!!!!!"

Tommy's instructions left off right there.

But I was raging on primal autopilot.

Finally removing my left arm from around her shoulder, I grabbed a condom off the night table, ripped it open with my teeth, and rolled it onto my erection with one swift swoop...

"OhhhhhhYesFuckMe!" she pleaded. "Yes, fuck me!"

I dove inside her and pumped with a frenzy...

Her hips and entire body yielded and bent to my exact desire, contouring perfectly to the natural shape I evoked with my elbows, hips, and pelvic thrusts...

She was utterly pliable...

Completely an instrument of pleasure to mold and receive me...

It was not long before I approached my own climax...

I had a momentary inclination to hold back and prolong the intercourse...

But I yielded to natural forces and let go with a groan...

Only to be most utterly surprised to hear her moan another "AhhhhhhGoddddddddddddAhhhhh!" and feel the convulsions accompanying A HOT WET EXPLOSION AROUND MY PENIS...

Near-scalding liquid splashed my balls and the base of my penis...

This COMPLETELY NEW AND DIFFERENT SEXUAL STIMULUS intensified my orgasm...

Thrilling me with the surge of her orgasmic energy...

As we pumped and thrust our hips into each other's...

Squeezing and sweating and swishing tongue kisses deep with animal passion...

And looking in each other's eyes to see an amazingly deep level of INTIMACY...

The result of some PRIMAL, ANIMAL BOND like never before...

And with its power we now saw the world through adrenaline-powered NEW EYES.

When our breathing began to slow and our minds began to clear I said, "Wow!"

She said, "Oh my God!"

I said, "Have you ever...?"

She shook her head.

"This was my first time too."

"What was that?" she asked in total awe.

"It was female ejaculation. I wrote a book about it with my friend..."

"You wrote a book about this????!?!!!!!!!! Oh my God! This is incredible!!!!! Everyone should be doing this!!!!!"

"I know," I said. "That was completely amazing. Totally different from anything I've ever felt before. More intense."

"Totally," she agreed. Then she said, "Clint, I love you."

I looked into her eyes, deep into her soul, and said, "I love you too."

We kissed and hugged until we fell asleep in each other's arms...

And we stayed wrapped and coiled tightly together all night long.

REVIEW QUIZ

1. The last place you ever want to talk with your lover about trying new sex techniques is ___ _____.

2. ___, _____ _____lighting and a ___, _____ bed are essential elements of the comfortable and erotic environment you should establish when learning about female ejaculations.

3. Paying very special attention to unusual parts of a person's body makes that person feel _____.

4. Name three unusual places to touch your lover, and three unusual ways to touch them.

5. If you are "stuck in your head" during lovemaking – or at any time – how can you "get out of your head"?

6. Before touching a woman's vagina, you should make sure that she is adequately _____ and _____.

7. The key sign of a woman's arousal is a sexy, _____ _____ of her hips.

8. Body language that builds trust includes: keeping your __ _____ her shoulder the whole time, and giving her _____ _____ as she progresses toward ejaculation.

9. Three ways to stimulate the G-spot with your fingers include: _____, _____, and _____.

2
SIMULTANEOUS ECSTASY

THE NEW SEX EXPERIENCE

Beth and I remained coiled tightly together for the next few months, sharing the intensity and primal connection of this New Sex Experience, on average, once a week – it was just too intense to do more often than that.

During these months of exploration and practice, I discovered how to SHARE SIMULTANEOUS ORGASMS EVERY TIME.

Once I brought Beth into a series of ejaculations and G-spot orgasms, the spark of one person's orgasm and ejaculation was just like throwing a switch for the other person.

It didn't matter if I came first, or she did – THE SHOCK OF ONE PERSON'S ORGASMIC ENERGY PULLED THE OTHER PERSON "OVER THE WALL."

Never had I enjoyed so much consistently reliable great sex…

My sexuality and her sexuality got into a major FLOW…

And so did our careers.

Beth gave my manuscript to a friend of hers who sold books to the movie studios. He sent it to a friend of his in New York City who had sold over 400 nonfiction books to major publishers…

Three weeks later, Simon & Schuster bought the publishing rights for the United Kingdom.

Phil and I produced and co-starred in one of my scripts, which we shot on video for a grand total of $97.92, and our "$100 Movie" got written up in the *Hollywood Reporter* under the headline "Watch Out Robert Rodriguez!"

That led to two paid screenwriting assignments from Hollywood producers…

A new high-powered agent representing me along with his clients Kirstie Alley, Jane Seymour, and James Brolin…

And a new entertainment attorney who was "the point man for all the deals done by Stallone, Schwarzenegger, and Jean-Claude Van Damme."

Beth felt the impact of our New Sex power as well: Seven of her clients became on-air series regulars that fall – she was RAKING IN the dough!

Our lives were firing on all cylinders, and this new sexual power was like having a 24-valve Ferrari engine under the hood.

Then Beth got pregnant.

We stopped having sex because she was always too sick...

She had the baby with a C-section...

Then was too tender and sore to have any sex at all for a few more months after that...

Simon & Schuster published the book without my name on the cover because "Single-author books sell better than two-author books..."

All my script projects and deals stalled in Development Hell...

I ran out of money and started driving a cab to pay bills...

And my grandmother died.

ROCK BOTTOM

Two months after my grandmother died, Beth kicked me out of the house and broke up with me. From the time she got pregnant until we broke up, we never again shared female ejaculations or simultaneous ejaculations.

I didn't realize it at the time, but this had a terribly destructive interruption of my natural energy flow.

I mean, here I was – a man who had somehow found the way to bring a very potent and powerful energy force into his life – and then all of a sudden, it was gone.

Think about the impact on an 747 that was flying through the sky above Hollywood if you suddenly removed its source of jet fuel.

Even if you gave it super-unleaded gasoline, its engines would still sputter and grind to a halt...

And that high-flying jet would C-R-A-S-H!

Thus began a three-year downward spiral in which I came as close to becoming an alcoholic as anyone would ever want to come...

I became celibate...

Couldn't get work as a writer for hire...

My amazing spec screenplays and the books I was passionate about got passed over...

I got stuck in the rut of driving a cab on Friday and Saturday nights, barely making ends meet on my earnings of $400 a week...

Hating my life, myself, and pretty much everyone I met.

I certainly had no interest in giving any woman pleasure...

Let alone sharing ultimate pleasure with anyone.

I was living a life of total solitude and self-imposed deprivation...

My home was a tiny sailboat – less than two hundred square feet of space...

I was washing my dishes with a hose out on the dock...

And walking up a ramp, going 150 feet to the public restrooms of the marina, every time I had to take a crap.

There was truly nowhere to go but up.

TUESDAY'S SUGGESTION

After enduring about two and a half years of this deplorable existence, I was driving a leased taxicab in Santa Monica when I got a call over the radio to "pick up Tuesday on 14th and Wilshire." I waited in front of the address until out came a scalding hot little redhead in a short skirt and low-cut top.

She had me take her to a hotel on Santa Monica Boulevard, and told me to come back for her in an hour. I did. And during the ride back to her house, she explained that she wasn't a hooker and never did anything with her "escort clients," and we somehow got into a conversation about my book and the techniques for giving any woman ultimate pleasure.

"You should do an infomercial," she said. "If you can really do that G-spot stuff on women I could hook you up with some of my clients who have a lot of money, they could finance a video, sell it on TV, and you'd make a fortune."

That got me thinking…

I called Tommy and asked him if he was interested in doing a video. By this point he had decided that being a "sex expert" was adversely affecting his career as a society photographer in Philadelphia. He didn't want to be involved with any new sex projects or even with publicizing the book anymore.

So I made a deal to pay him a royalty on the sales of a video I'd make using the techniques in our book. I tried to raise a lot of money to produce a video, and a lot of people made me a lot of promises, and nobody came through.

Ultimately I decided to do a super-low-budget video along the lines of the "$100 Movie" I had produced with Phil, just to get the project off the ground. All I needed, really, was a girl.

"NEW SEX NOW"

I figured that finding a girl to do a sex video in Hollywood would be no problem. But for a man who is not "in the flow," nothing is easy.

I called World Modeling Agency, the major porn-star agency I'd read about in *LA Magazine*, and made an appointment. When I got inside their offices on the second floor of a small walkup on Van Nuys Boulevard, I showed the owner, Jim South, the paperback of Tommy's and my book. He raised his eyebrows as if he were impressed. Then I explained that I wanted a girl who would let me do the techniques on her and share simultaneous ejaculations with me during intercourse.

Jim said, "Okay, you want one girl for a boy-girl scene, working one day. The agency fee will be sixty dollars for that one day's work. Whatever you and the performer agree upon is what you will pay her directly."

I wrote out a personal check for $60.00, and Jim pointed me to a huge pile of photo albums, each one about six inches thick, stuffed with Polaroids, 8-by-10s, and video box covers of every porn starlet and wannabe in Hollywood. "Pick out the girls you like, write their names down on a pad of paper, and give that list to my assistant. Then we'll get in touch with the girls and see which ones can squirt for you." I compiled a list of fifteen, and left them my number.

Three weeks later I still hadn't heard a peep, so I called Jim South to find out what was going on. His assistant answered the call, I told her who I was and why I was calling, and then she asked for my mailing address.

"I called all the girls on your list," she explained. "Only a couple of them knew how to squirt, and those girls only do that with people they regularly work with (either boyfriends or husbands), so they're not interested in doing this scene. We'll be refunding your agency fee in the mail."

It seemed that of all the porn stars in Hollywood, only a tiny percentage could "squirt," and those girls only did it with their regular partner because it was TOO INTIMATE to share with just anyone.

One of my friends suggested that I try searching on the Internet. "Look up tantra." I did, and at about two in the morning I discovered GoddessTemple.com – one of my favorite sites on the World Wide Web.

This is basically a website where professional tantra Goddesses advertise to connect with men, women, and couples interested in learning various tantric rituals and ceremonies with and from experienced tantrikas. There are also pages featuring explanations of the various ceremonies, as well as reviews written by clients about experiences with individual Goddesses.

I looked through the collection of over fifty Goddesses' photo galleries, selected about twenty-five who looked attractive enough for the video, and sent each of them the following email:

SUBJECT: Sacred Quest for a Love Goddess
    I pray you are receptive to the spirit of this message.
    Having written *Ultimate Female Orgasms* (Simon & Schuster, UK), my devotion to the awesome powers of the Goddess spot and amrita are well documented. My approach and audience, however, have been mainstream rather than tantric, so you may not be familiar with my work even though over 75,000 copies have been sold throughout the world.
    A new experiential video is in final stages of preparation, with the intention of finding even larger audiences for the intensely spiritual wonders of female ejaculation and simultaneous ejaculation.
    This video requires the participation of a Love Goddess. Someone familiar with these intense experiences and willing to share this natural energy and beauty with the world.
    My book and earlier efforts as an environmental artist have attracted huge national and international media attention, as this work no doubt will. If you would be gracious enough to telephone me at (310) 821-83XX or reply by email at your earliest convenience, I'd welcome an opportunity to meet with you and discuss the possible opportunities and synergies this project could have for you.
    Sincerely and respectfully,
    Clint

The first Goddess to respond was Mare Simone, who replied by email with a phone number. When I dialed the number at two in the afternoon, a very sultry female voice answered, "Hello."

I said, "This is Clint, may I speak with Goddess Mare?"

She said, "This is Goddess Mare."

I said, "Did I wake you?"

"No."

I said, "What are you doing?"

She laughed and said, "I'm just lying here in bed ... pleasuring myself."

I said, "Oh, how wonderful!" I immediately got a hard-on, hopped in bed, unzipped my fly, and started pleasuring myself. "I was so glad to receive your email regarding my sacred quest for a Love Goddess."

"Tell me about your project," she said breathily.

"A few years ago I wrote a book about female ejaculation and the G-spot."

"In tantra we call it the Goddess spot, and refer to female ejaculation as amrita."

"So you know about female ejaculation?" I asked brightly.

"Oh yes," she purred. "One of my former lovers, Dr. Gary Schubach, did an extensive study on amrita, and I was a participant in the research."

"So you can ejaculate?"

"Of course. Every woman can. Just not all women do."

"That's exactly the point of this project! Basically, my book explains how to help any woman experience amrita. And in this video project I want to demonstrate exactly what to do, and then how to go beyond that to achieve simultaneous ejaculations."

"That sounds like a fun project, Clint. I've been ejaculating for many years. It's one of the most beautiful, important, and powerful aspects of sexuality, and I support any project that brings this vital knowledge to women and to the men who love them."

"Thank you! It's so great to find someone who understands the power and beauty of what I'm trying to do. Do you think you might have any interest in perhaps being my Love Goddess in the video?" I asked timidly yet hopefully.

"Oh Clint," she said. "I probably would have a few years ago. But now I'm just too old and fat to do anything like that."

I said, "Oh, Goddess! Are you sure?"

"Yes, Clint, I'm afraid I am."

"That's too bad. Especially to find someone like yourself who's so experienced and comfortable with amrita."

"You should talk to Dr. Corynna Clarke. She's someone who might do your video."

"I actually sent her an email, but she hasn't replied."

"Just be patient," Mare said. "Corynna is very busy."

"I will," I said. "But in the meantime, would you consider giving a testimonial or interview for the video, just talking about your experiences with amrita?"

"It would be my pleasure."

A few days later I drove up to Goddess Mare's love temple in the Hollywood Hills. I was instructed not to arrive earlier than our appointed time, because she would be with a client. I was sure to wear my sexiest Armani Exchange shirt, and just the right amount of five-o'clock shadow on my face.

I knocked on the wooden door of her 1920s Spanish hacienda, and was greeted by a sexy, exotic, slightly Hispanic-looking woman in her early forties. She wore long curly brown locks of hair down past her shoulders, shiny lip-gloss, dark eyeliner, a purple diaphanous blouse, and a dark brown silk paisley skirt.

She opened the door as I said, "Hello, Goddess, I'm Clint."

Serenely, she said, "Hello, Clint. Please come in."

The interior of her apartment was quirky, yet not over the top. Erotic prints and drawings were displayed on the walls, and there were hanging beads, candles, and erotic books and videos on her shelves. She offered me a cup of mint tea, and I accepted.

While the water boiled, she showed me beautiful nude photos and close-up pictures of glistening amrita shooting out of her *yoni* (the tantric word for vagina.) Indeed, she did look a little younger and thinner in those images.

Then I set up my video camera and recorded her testimonial about how she had learned how to ejaculate from Charles and Caroline Muir, and how she was sure, after having worked with hundreds of women during her professional tantra career, that all women could experience amrita and "sacred spot" orgasms.

At the conclusion of the interview, Mare said, "I really need you to get going now, Clint. I have a client coming in a few minutes, and I need to prepare. But it's been a pleasure meeting you. And maybe we could get together sometime and 'trade sessions.' "

"Trade sessions?"

"You know – get wet!"

"Oh, that sounds like a lot of fun – I'd love to!"

She gave me a long, luscious hug, then said, "Call me and we'll set it up. And call Corynna."

I MEET THE GREAT ONE

I left a message for Dr. Corynna Clarke saying that Mare had told me to call her. She returned my call the next day, and we agreed to meet at the Cow coffee shop in Venice.

Dr. Clarke drove up in a maroon Corvette, looking very attractive in a brown and cream paisley silk blouse and shiny lip-gloss. She asked about my vision for the New Sex Now project, I told her it was about female ejaculation, the Goddess spot, and simultaneous ejaculation. She told me she loved having simultaneous ejaculations with her lovers, and that she also believed all women could ejaculate, and asked how much the video shoot would pay. I mentioned a fee of $500, and she immediately explained that she had already appeared in a Sacred Sexuality video a few years earlier, with one of her other lovers, and flat out denied any interest in being in New Sex Now, although she gave me blessings of the Goddess for my worthy efforts. That was fine with me because I was NOT THE SLIGHTEST BIT ATTRACTED TO HER, and I was really hoping that she didn't want to do the video because I didn't feel any chemistry with her.

A couple nights later, after my regular visitation with my daughter, I drove up to a pub in Silver Lake to meet another Goddess named Anthea.

Anthea was a skinny Australian blonde with long, dirty hair and bad teeth. She ordered a Calistoga water, which she left untouched on the table after immediately declining any interest in participating in the video. She wished me luck, suggested I call Dr. Corynna Clarke, and left. That was fine with me, as I wasn't the least bit attracted to Anthea either.

I felt it was IMPERATIVE that I should have REAL CHEMISTRY with the woman in the video; otherwise it just wouldn't work.

The following Thursday, I drove back up to the Hollywood Hills for my appointment to trade sessions and get wet with Mare.

She looked even sexier this time, wearing no bra beneath her silk see-through blouse, and seeming relaxed and not pressed for time. We sat on the couch sipping tea, then started French-kissing. She was a good kisser, and I was getting very aroused when the phone rang and her answering machine picked up the call.

She listened to the woman's voice screening through the machine, then grabbed the phone and told the woman, "I'm with someone right now, on a date. No, not a client – Clint." Then she listened for a while and said, "Okay, let me call you back." Hanging up the phone she said to me, "Clint, I don't know if you'd be interested in attending or not, but we're invited to join in an ejaculation ceremony at the love temple of another Goddess."

I said, "What's an ejaculation ceremony?"

"Oh, three or four Goddesses sitting around ejaculating and tripping on mushrooms."

"Gee," I said sarcastically. "I'm not sure if that would be any fun."

She said, equally sarcastically, "I understand how that might not be any fun for you."

Then I said, "But you know how I feel about amrita, and if there's any way that I can support the Goddess, I'm happy to be of service."

She said, "That's the spirit, Clint!"

And so Goddess Mare and I set off for the ejaculation ceremony at Goddess Anthea's love temple.

ANTHEA'S LOVE TEMPLE

In a very posh poured-concrete building way out on Franklin Avenue, in the far eastern foothills of Hollywood, lay the love temple of Goddess Anthea.

Goddess Mare and I were greeted at the front door by our hostess. Anthea was in a considerably better mood than when I had met her previously. And she was also topless.

She led us into the living room, where Dr. Corynna Clarke and another Goddess were topless too, sitting on a futon in a corner of the large and otherwise empty living room, smoking pot from a large purple glass bong.

Mare and the Goddesses greeted one another with kisses. Then I was introduced and shook hands first with Dr. Clarke, then with the stunning Russian Goddess Natalia, whose large, full, succulent breasts had captivated me from the first instant I laid eyes upon them.

Mare and I each accepted the offer of a hit of pot on the bong. Then, at Dr. Clarke's suggestion, we formed a large mandala, sitting Indian-style in a circle on the futon, with our knees touching, holding hands with the people on either side of us. I was seated between Mare and Anthea, and I could hardly keep my eyes off Goddess Natalia.

SETTING AN INTENTION

"I think it's important for each of us to begin by stating an intention for this ceremony," said Dr. Corynna Clarke. Everyone nodded ascent. "It is my intention," she began, "for this ceremony to bring the spirit of the Goddess into each of us, so that we can all benefit from the love and the power of her sacred energy, bringing more fulfillment and passion and abundance and beauty – and especially abundance – into all of our lives…"

The other Goddesses said, "Amen, sister!" and giggled.

When it was my turn I announced my intention: "To be of support to the Great Goddess and to be of support in any way I can to the power and the beauty of amrita."

INVOCATION

Dr. Clarke pronounced an invocation for the ceremony, "Calling forth the power of the Goddess of the North, and the Goddess of the South, the Goddess of the Moon and of the Stars, Shakti and Shiva, the blessed Earth Mother, and of the Fairies and Spirits of protection to offer strength and love to everyone in our sacred circle. Amen."

When the preliminaries were over, we sat in silence for a few seconds, everyone taking in the sacredness of the space, then Mare said joyously, "Okay, let's get naked!"

And all the Goddesses stripped off their clothing with gleeful giggles.

There I was, wearing a pair of Gap khakis and my sexy Armani Exchange shirt. I said, "Excuse me, I'll be right back."

I went to the bathroom to take a leak and undress. I was very nervous. I had about half a hard-on, which I thought was the right amount of arousal to display, not too anxious, cool yet still "representing." I looked into my eyes reflected in the bathroom mirror, smiled, and said, "Way to go, Clint!"

Returning to the living room I noticed a bulletin board on the wall of an alcove next to the bathroom, on which were thumb-tacked about twenty "appointment cards" showing men's names, phone numbers, and ceremonies, such as "Goddess Worship" and "Male Sacred Spot" along with dollar amounts of $160 and up.

CLIMB ABOARD THE TRAIN & HANG ON!

When I got back to the living room, the Goddesses were all rubbing and massaging one another in a straight line on the futon, and Mare said, "It's a train, Clint – find a place to climb aboard and hang on!"

I dropped my clothes in a pile by the wall, and slowly moved behind Goddess Natalia. She was sitting at the end of the train, massaging Dr. Clarke's back while Dr. Clarke was going down on Mare and massaging her sacred spot while Anthea massaged Mare's shoulder's and made out with her.

NATURAL ANIMAL

Very slowly, I nuzzled in against Goddess Natalia's back and started to give her a sensual shoulder massage. It was very animalistic the way she looked back at me with a casual yet decisive side-glance over her shoulder, and allowed me to approach her, totally naked and semierect, without ever having exchanged a word.

After a few minutes of massaging her shoulders, I moved my massage to her biceps and triceps, then I worked my fingers along her ribs, into the small of her back, and down to her hips.

By this point, Mare was making all kinds of aroused noises, with Anthea and Dr. Clarke making similar and sympathetic sounds. Dr. Clarke got on her hands and knees, with her butt and yoni raised up right in front of my face and Goddess Natalia face.

Natalia was being timid, massaging Corynna's hips, so I licked my right thumb, and slowly extended it toward Dr. Clarke's yoni. She responded immediately with a moan of relief as my thumb entered her yoni temple and sought out the bumps and ridges of her Goddess spot.

Natalia had seemed nervous when I reached out to touch Corynna, but she relaxed when Dr. Clarke started moving her hips back and forth sexually around my thumb.

I was honored that she was allowing me to touch her there, and I tried to be as gentle and respectful as I could be, while still remembering to keep my other hand moving sensually on the naked body of the powder-white-skinned Russian Goddess. And I began to press my now raging hard-on up against her spine, and let my fingers move from her hips to her thighs…

Gently swooshing over the creamy whiteness of her inner thighs…

While Dr. Clarke humped my thumb…

Then I SLOWLY cupped Natalia's entire vagina with my palm…

Holding it over the entrance to her yoni temple, allowing her to feel the warmth of my flesh…

She didn't seem to be getting very aroused…

But she wasn't pushing me away, either…

Not even when I touched her vaginal lips with my fingers, and <u>slowly rubbed up and down the length of them</u>...

Starting to <u>feel the wetness of her juices on the pads of my fingers</u>...

With Mare's moans growing louder and louder...

Echoes of arousal from Anthea...

And Dr. Clarke's hip thrusts around my helpful hand increasing intensity...

Then I made a very visible show of licking my middle finger next to Natalia's face...

Before lowering it between her hips...

And curling inside her yoni temple.

Now I had my fingers on the sacred Goddess spots of two different Goddesses...

Dr. Clarke was going CRAZY...

So was Mare...

And Natalia seemed to be on the verge of relaxing under my touch...

When I felt huge contractions inside Dr. Clarke...

THAT BEAUTIFUL "SQUISH-SQUISH-SQUISH"

Then I heard that old, beautiful sound of ejaculatory liquid squish-squish-squishing from Mare's midsection in the middle of the train...

Dr. Clarke SQUIRTED out a hot, wet burst of amrita around my thumb, splashing into Natalia's lap...

I was breathing hard...

Grinding my hard penis into Natalia's back...

Fingering her sacred spot...

Trying to be conscious and conscientious and caring while being consumed with erotic excitement...

Then Dr. Clarke turned around to look at me with Mare's sacred fluids all over her mouth and chin and said, "How'd you like THAT simultaneous ejaculation, Clint?"

I said, "Yeah!"

Soon thereafter, the intercom rang, and Anthea went to buzz in Dr. Clarke's boyfriend, Evan. He was greeted with kisses from her and Anthea, then he and the little Australian ran off to a Jacuzzi on the patio, from whence we soon heard moans and squeals of erotic joy.

Corynna and Mare smoked more pot from the bong, and sipped champagne until Anthea and Evan came back inside and started fucking on the floor next to the futon.

Meanwhile, I lay down on the futon beside Goddess Natalia, then moved my body between her legs to go down on her with my best tonguing techniques while my index and middle finger continued to stimulate her sacred spot.

THE KEY TO GREAT CUNNILINGUS

The key to great cunnilingus is to suck and stimulate the woman's clitoris like it's a miniature penis.

LICK & FLICK

For so many years I just licked and flicked at the clitoris with my tongue, until I stumbled on the concept of sucking it…

Sucking the clitoris until it engorges with blood as a minierection, and moving it up and down, in and out, between my lips…

Actually moving my head in and out over the minipenis that is the erect clit.

Now with the beautiful milky white Russian Goddess splayed before me, and with Anthea and Dr. Clarke's boyfriend fucking five feet away, I focused all my concentration on sucking and licking the blonde yoni temple before me.

After about twenty minutes, Mare and Dr. Clarke came back to the futon, and Mare kissed and rubbed Natalia's beautiful breasts while I pleasured her with my mouth.

Five minutes later, Mare got down beside me and we both went down on Natalia, licking and kissing her yoni together, kissing each other's mouths – it was such heaven…

But Natalia would not let go and "let it flow."

When Mare and I stopped going down on her, we went on either side of Natalia to hug all together, and Mare asked, "Why don't you let go, Natalia?"

Natalia started crying softly. "I have never been able to have amrita with another person. Only by myself."

We held her and comforted her while Anthea and Dr. Clarke's boyfriend pumped their way to moaning climaxes in front of us…

Then people started putting their clothes on…

And Natalia said, "But Clint hasn't been satisfied…"

Mare and Dr. Clarke looked at each other and said, "Well, that's how it goes…. Sometimes it's just about serving the Goddess."

I said, "That's fine with me. It's my honor to serve the Goddess!"

Dr. Clarke said, "He's a good one, Mare. Where'd you find him?" Mare laughed, and Dr. Clarke addressed me, saying, "You're going to be very popular in the Goddess community."

We got dressed and said our good nights, not asking for or exchanging phone numbers. I drove Mare home and thanked her for a beautiful evening. During the whole drive back to Marina del Rey my head buzzed with the feeling that I was on top of the world.

MELODY X

The next night was a Friday, and I got a radio call to pick up Tuesday in my taxi at her house on 14th Street. She was looking sexy as usual, dressed for a date with a client who was meeting her at the Ivy, one of LA's fanciest restaurants.

I told her that as a result of her encouragement I had decided to make a microbudget movie about my G-spot techniques, but was having trouble finding a Love Goddess for the production.

Tuesday said, "You should talk to my friend Melody X. She'll do your video."

"Does she have squirt?"

"She does everything! Her specialty is doing small parties, like eight or nine guys."

I said, "Cool. Is she beautiful and sexy like you?"

"She was a Penthouse Pet. Give me your phone number, and I'll have her call you."

Melody X called, and we set a date to meet for lunch at Izzy's Deli on Wilshire Boulevard, a block from Tuesday's house in Santa Monica. I was sure to wear that very same sexy Armani X shirt and the exact right amount of five-o'clock shadow.

Blonde, sexy thin, with perfectly proportioned big C-cup breasts and big lips that shined and shimmered with salmon-pink gloss, she arrived about twenty minutes late, wearing a short yellow skirt, a peach-colored tube top, and four-inch stiletto heels.

Every single eye in the restaurant watched as she walked from the front door to my table and sat down. This girl was the Goods, and not only did she know it and know that everyone else knew it, but she also had a unique kind of self-confidence that you can only get from earning lots of money as a result of your sexual desirability.

I stood up from the booth as she approached, extended my hand, and said in my sexiest deep voice, "I'm Clint."

She shook my hand and said, "Nice to meet you, Clint." Then she oozed onto the bench of the booth. I sat down, leaving about two feet of space between us, and basked in her intense and amazing sexuality.

When the waiter came, I ordered a niçoise salad and iced tea. She got a bowl of chicken noodle soup and hot tea. The food arrived almost immediately, and while I ate my salad, I enjoyed watching her suck each and every noodle that she ate individually off the spoon. This woman was truly working me with her sexual power!

I showed her a copy of my book and told her about my intentions for the video. She said, "It sounds like this is going to be a very spiritual project, Clint."

I said, "I am a great devotee of the Goddess."

She said, "Good, because I would only do a project like this if it was going to be spiritual."

Taking a risk, I said as casually as I could, "You know, Melody, a project like this is dependent upon chemistry between the models. Now, I feel a lot of chemistry for you. Do you feel an attraction for me as well?"

She considered the question for a few moments, then nodded very seriously, yet with no anxiousness whatsoever. As hard as I was playing to be cool, she was even cooler, with the arctic chill of coolness about sex that can only come from getting paid to have sex all the time.

I said, "It's great that we both feel that, but you never know what's going to happen in bed."

She said, "That's true."

"As much as the first time can be very special, do you think it would be possible for us to meet sometime in private, to see if we really do have the kind of chemistry I'm looking for together in bed? Sort of a rehearsal or audition?"

She said, "That could be possible. You could come up to my house one afternoon, when my boyfriend isn't around."

I said, "Do you live with your boyfriend?"

She said, "Not really."

I said, "How about Thursday afternoon?"

"That sounds fine," she said, slurping a medium-length noodle off her spoon. "But why don't you call me Thursday to make sure."

As we exited the restaurant, once again the electrical charge of the whole dining room went off the scale as every eyeball locked onto Melody's porn-star body and overall sexual intensity.

She kissed me goodbye on the lips, just a peck, and said, "See you Thursday, Clint," then sashayed up the block toward Tuesday's house.

Thursday morning around eleven, I called Melody and said with my deepest sexiest voice, "Hi, Melody, this is Clint."

She said, "Hi, Clint."

Long pause.

I said, "Am I going to have the pleasure of seeing you later this afternoon?"

She said, "I'm sorry, Clint, it's just not going to work for this afternoon."

What a surprise!

I said, "That's all right, Melody. Why don't we just go ahead and schedule the shoot. I'm sure the chemistry will be fine. I mean, you do have female ejaculations, don't you?"

"As often as I can!"

SHOOTING *NEW SEX NOW*

She agreed to meet me at the Oceana Hotel in Santa Monica at 2 p.m. the following Sunday. She showed up two hours late. But she looked as hot as Main Street in Midland, Texas, at high noon on the Fourth of July.

I was lightheaded from losing weight to be in top shape for my first public on-screen nude sex scene, and nervous as hell about having to perform, having to get an erection on camera, and having to pay Melody $1400 and another $400 for the suite. It was a HUGE amount of money for me at that point in my life.

Thank God Melody X turned out to be supercool!

I borrowed digital video cameras from friends, and set them up at different places in the bedroom.

She took a bath and relaxed for about an hour, then she came out and joined me in the big bed.

I gave her the full-body massage described earlier, starting with the fingers…

Working my way up the arms…

Up to her neck…

Her skull…

Down the front of her body…

Teasing the nipples…

Avoiding the vagina…

Down the thighs…

All the way to her feet…

I don't have a foot fetish, but I really wanted to give her my all, so I sucked on her toes, sucked on her arches…

Turned her over and licked and sucked up the backs of her legs…

<u>Especially on the creases behind her knees…</u>

Then I worked my way up, licking and sucking her thighs…

And then, staring at her gorgeous ass writhing and undulating before my eyes, I created a new technique.

BREATHE ON HER VAGINA

I *LOVE* when you get to this point in the Ultimate Erotic Massage – the woman is usually SOOOOOOO TURNED ON…

She's SOOOOOOO wanting you to go down on her…

Especially when you're licking her inner thighs…

So, lo and behold, there I was, licking the sweet, luscious inner thighs of Melody X…

Her neatly shaved landing strip undulating before my eyes, filling me with passion…

I just got as close as I could to her swollen lips and BREATHED ON HER VAGINA…

For a long, long, long, long time…

Breathing hot breaths with my mouth about an inch from her vaginal lips…

With her hips bucking and pushing her sweet yoni toward my mouth…

Trying to make contact and get satisfaction…

But I was a spatial artist…

Always maintaining that crucial distance…

Teasing her with the proximity…

Resisting every urge of temptation that screamed in my mind to go down on that fresh, tasty immaculate sex thing before me…

GNAWING BUTTOCKS

After teasing her like that practically FOREVER…

I slowly continued my way by gnawing into her buttocks…

Breathing on her anus…

(And GOD that anus was gorgeous – clean, puckered, and calling me to lick it…)

Then kissing and licking my way up through the small of her back…

Up along her spine…

Straddling her butt, sitting lightly on it, and gently (subconsciously) rubbing my hard penis into the crack of her ass…

Massaging up to her shoulders…

Her sinewy neck muscles…

Turning her over…

With my left arm around her shoulder…

Looking for and receiving that RELAXED HUG from her…

Noticing that SEXY, WAVELIKE MOTION OF HER HIPS…

And then, for the very first time, I kissed her…

It started as a gentle tongue kiss…

But she quickly opened her mouth wide to deepen it into a very erotic and full-on French kiss…

I thought to myself, *Wow, this woman is really going to let me have sex with her! This is really going to happen!*

Gently rubbing the SECRET HOT SPOT above the pubic hair, right below the bellybutton, for sixty seconds…

CUPPING THE ENTIRE VAGINA with my palm…

Maintaining just enough distance for her to feel the heat of my flesh…

Her lips were more like mounds than flaps, so with one finger on each lip, I slowly spread open her vagina…

Softly rubbing up and down the length of the lips…

Getting her juices on my fingertips…

Before slowly entering her vagina with one finger…

And simultaneously giving her an EXTRA HUG as a body-language cue to reinforce the trust…

WHICH FINGER TO USE

According to Dr. Clarke, in tantra there is a relationship between each of the fingers and the various chakras of the body. The ring finger is directly connected to the heart chakra, and that's why tantra practitioners advise using that finger to make first contact with the Goddess spot.

From a Western standpoint, I recommend using the ring finger because IT'S WEAKER THAN THE INDEX OR MIDDLE FINGER.

You want to USE THE LIGHTEST POSSIBLE TOUCH, and by handicapping yourself with the weakest of your long fingers you'll be able to reach the spot without putting too much pressure on it.

I held my finger motionless on the bumps and ridges of her front vaginal wall for a long time...

Letting her G-spot feel my finger...

Letting it get familiar with my touch...

After more than a minute of stillness, I began to stimulate her sacred spot...

I alternated between PRESSING HER G-SPOT...

MOVING MY FINGER UP AND DOWN, IN AND OUT...

MAKING CIRCLES AROUND IT...

And reaching all the way to the back of her vaginal vault to MAKE SWOOSHES AROUND HER CERVIX.

CERVICAL SEX

All the way at the back of the vagina is a hard, cartilage-like protrusion that, during childbirth, dilates to an opening of as much as 10 centimeters. It is through this opening that the baby must pass on its way out of the womb. At the other end of the reproduction process, the semen must enter through this opening on their way to fertilize the eggs during sex.

The cervix is an extremely erotic part of the woman's interior architecture.

I really enjoyed swooshing around Melody X's cervix with first one finger...

Then two...

Of course giving her an extra hug as I introduced my second finger inside her...

Her breathing was getting heavier and faster...

And so was mine...

But for some reason it was feeling forced to me...

Like she was embellishing her level of arousal with fake enthusiasm...

And soon she asked to take a "pee break."

When she came back to the bed, she had a bottle of WET PLATINUM lubricant in her hands, and she said, "Why don't you try some of this on me, Clint," as she handed me the bottle and laid down on her stomach.

I squirted a little into my palm, and started to warm it up by rubbing my hands together. She said, "No, no – pour it on!"

So I slathered up her butt with the Wet Platinum...

Really drenched it in that silky, sexy lube...

And the result was instantaneous and profound...

I put my THUMB inside her...

And she was DRENCHED...

Her hips began grinding...

Soon she went from CONTRACTIONS of the vaginal muscles...

To CONVULSIONS of the entire VAGINA and PELVIC REGION...

A quick and inspiring PRE-EJACULATORY FLOOD-RUSH...

Followed almost immediately by a huge GUSH of amrita and unmistakably authentic MOANS OF PLEASURE...

"Oh yeah! I want you to come for me like that again!" I told her.

She did.

I was loving it...

And she said, "You want to have an orgasm with me like that?"

I said, "Yeah!" and put on a condom.

I entered her from behind, dog-style, and sure enough, the energy of her next ejaculation triggered my own...

And, lo and behold, there we were, coming together...

The very first time we had sex.

It was exhilarating to share that with her...

Gratifying to have instant success using the techniques with a total stranger...

And a relief to have actually captured it on tape after going through the three-and-a-half-month ordeal between the time when I first decided to make the video and that fateful day.

ANAL EROTICA

After we climaxed, we caught our breath, I turned off the cameras, and laid down next to her on the bed. She asked me if I wanted to take some Ecstasy, and I said, "Sure."

She crawled across the bed to the phone to dial a friend of hers, who agreed to bring some over.

As she was on her hands and knees talking to the girl on the phone, I crawled up behind her and started munching on her beautiful, clean, puckered ass.

It was so delicious!

I was licking and sucking it...

Licking her vagina and her ass with big long licks...

And she was SOOOOO loving it.

I munched on her for a LONNNNNNNNGGGGGGG time, then I asked her, "Can you deep throat?"

She said, "Tuesday taught me how."

"She did? What does Tuesday know about deep throat?"

Melody said, "Tuesday is the queen of sucking cock."

I said, "Would you deep throat me for a while on your hands and knees? I love it in that position."

ORAL SERVITUDE

My favorite position for a woman to be in while giving me head is on her hands and knees while I'm on my knees in front of her.

She is serving me totally in that position.

Visually...

Orally…

Conceptually: She is beneath me, at my knees…

I can control her body with my hands, with my elbows and forearms, and all the while I can see the beautiful heart shape of her ass in the air, the inward curve of her hips, the blonde tangle of her hair in my crotch…

And Melody gladly did it…

Sucking me for a good six or seven minutes, without a condom.

It wasn't the most satisfying deep throat I'd ever had…

But it was some excellent head…

Mostly because she was just SO FUCKING SEXY AND HOT LOOKING naked and sucking my naked cock for me like that…

And not because I was paying her to do it, either…

She was doing it because she wanted to do it…

Because I had given her three awesome orgasms…

And because we had real natural chemistry.

She was a sexual and sexy person, and we were a great pair together in bed.

My only regret of that night was that I didn't get that blowjob on video.

At some point the phone rang, and the front desk announced the arrival of Melody's friend Jillian with our X delivery.

ECSTASY & SEX DON'T MIX

It was after nine o'clock, so I ordered room service from Wolfgang Puck's Café. We ate quickly, then took the X and drank some champagne with Jillian, a very cool chick with a purple and blonde crewcut and low-key tattoos.

I asked her if she would shoot some footage of me and Melody getting it on, and she said she'd give it a try, although she wasn't a professional camerawoman.

Melody and I got naked and climbed into bed with Jillian behind one of the digital cameras, and with the aid of Melody's Wet Platinum, it wasn't long before she was once again in the thralls of a long series of ejaculations and G-spot orgasms.

After four more orgasms that Jillian captured with beautiful close-ups of Melody's face, she said, "Put it inside! I want you to put it inside me!"

I said, "Not yet."

The X was preventing me from getting an erection.

THE DRUG GOT ME STUCK IN MY HEAD...

And for that reason I recommend that you DO NOT USE ANY DRUGS when trying to have this kind of sensual lovemaking experience.

Drugs will trap you in your head, and will prevent you from experiencing all the natural sensations with your body.

The essential key to sensual lovemaking mastery is maximizing the level of your sensual experience.

Melody tried getting me aroused by giving me head...

But it was no use.

Jillian left, and when we watched the tapes, to my horror I saw for the first time that our beautiful experience of simultaneous ejaculations earlier in the afternoon was not useable footage: Our heads had gone out-of-frame, and you couldn't see our faces.

The stuff Jillian had shot was good, but it was only footage of Melody having orgasms.

The New Sex Experience was still essentially undocumented!

I was freaked.

Thank God Melody was so cool.

And thank God she was into me because I gave her so much hot sex...

And we had such a HOT CONNECTION.

She took me into the bedroom and started giving me a back rub.

I was so uptight and so nervous about fucking this whole thing up by not getting a good shot the first time and not being able to get an erection when Jillian was shooting us because I was high!

After about fifteen minutes of rubbing my back, Melody turned me over and went down on me...

It was near midnight...

The lights were dim...

KCRW was playing cool music on the radio...

And lo and behold...

My erection returned...

Much to my surprise and excitement, Melody climbed on top of me and put me inside her WITHOUT A CONDOM!

It was SO FAR OVER THE EDGE TO BE HAVING UNPROTECTED SEX WITH HER!

I was so scared...

And so exhilarated...

And so falling in love with her.

Maybe it was the X. Maybe it was the sex. Maybe it was the New Sex we shared. But we had SUCH AMAZING CHEMISTRY – and her having unprotected sex with me like that made me feel like she felt the connection too.

I said, "Thank God! It's about time I got to fuck you without a condom."

She said, "You didn't have to wait very long."

I said, "I've been waiting ever since we had lunch together."

She said, "Oh, poor baby, four whole days!"

Then we stopped talking and just kissed deeply while we made love until we fell asleep.

DESTINY

I've never been an early riser. But when you have a mission that you believe in, when you're working on your true life's purpose, when you're excited about what you're doing, it's easy to get out of bed in the morning.

All of a sudden, sometime around 7 a.m., I found myself curled naked in bed with my arms and legs wrapped around the sexy, naked blonde Penthouse Pet who went by the stage name of Melody X.

I disentangled myself as cautiously as possible from her limbs so as not to disturb her sleep, then put mini-DV tapes in the cameras, pressed their record buttons, and climbed back in bed.

She was lying on her stomach, so I crawled under the sheet and hung my head down over her butt to go down on her. I remember thinking to myself *Once I tried this on Beth, and she got pissed at me for waking her up – I hope Melody doesn't get pissed!*

Melody X did not get pissed. She got into it! Immediately!

She started pressing her vagina against my mouth…

Her juices flowed…

Hips gyrated with that sexy back-and-forth movement…

After a few minutes I climbed on top of her body and started massaging her G-spot with my thumb, in and out…

Using my EYES to watch the effect on her…

KISSING HER IN UNUSUAL WAYS AND PLACES – down her spine…

On her hipbone…

The small of her back…

LISTENING to the quickening of her heartbeat…

FEELING the softness of her skin…

Giving her NONVERBAL encouragement…

Grunting and moaning along with her own sounds of arousal...

"Come for me baby..." I growled...

THE "SWITCHING-OUT" TECHNIQUE

She said, "I want your cock!"

I said, "Yeah?"

She said, "Yeah! Give it to me!"

I got behind her doggy-style and enjoyed some deep, long bareback strokes inside her dripping wet vagina...

Then, summoning all the self-control I had, I pulled out my penis and went back to using my thumb on her G-spot.

This technique seemed to have an awesome impact on her arousal...

(Since then, I've used it many times, always with similarly powerful results.)

Switching back and forth one more time was enough to get her over the wall to where she once again – for something like the tenth time with me – was letting it flow.

Then I put it back inside of her and went to town, knowing that I was going to shoot an unprotected load inside of her, that we were going to share this most intimate and personal moment...

Sure enough, as I felt myself going into a state of orgasm, I said, "I'm gonna cum!"

Two seconds later she said, "Me too!"

My shot erupted deep within her and splashed her cervix with cum...

A second later you can hear her groan with orgasmic release...

And a hot, wet explosion of amrita soaked my cock and balls...

It was such a thrill! After the breakup with Beth, I never thought I'd be able to get so intimate with another woman – let alone with a woman as scaldingly hot and sexy as Melody.

I was <u>sure</u> I had impregnated her…

That she would bear the love child of this union…

My mind was racing…

Our baby would be a result of our shared destiny…

Our child's name should echo this moment…

Someday (when it was much older), I wanted to show the child the tape of its conception

I actually said "Destiny!" intending that to be the baby's name.

The moment was captured for sure. I was certain to keep our bodies in frame this time. We stayed locked together at the hips for many, many minutes, and I continued to pump and rejoice in a long orgasmic afterglow.

INFINITE ORGASM

During that experience with Melody, I realized for the first time that the sensations of orgasm continue as long as the man remains inside the woman.

And while lying there I realized for the first time that the afterglow of simultaneous ejaculations is an extremely heightened state of sensory awareness.

All of a sudden I became aware of the birds chirping in the trees outside our window…

I smelled the scent of orange blossoms in the air…

Felt the softness of expensive cotton sheets beneath us, and her silky smooth skin against my body…

I could taste the saltiness of my own saliva…

And the colors of the artwork on the wall above the bed seemed to be jumping out at me.

We stayed wrapped together like that for long time, until we fell asleep, and I woke some time later that morning to the sound of her running water for a bath…

I was in heaven, because I knew that I had accomplished a goal that had eluded me for months, that had almost escaped me through my own incompetence – but now it was done. Everything in my life was going to be different, and better.

■■

You're probably wondering if anything "developed" between me and Melody after that superintense sexual connection…

I called her the next day to thank her for a beautiful experience. She answered her cell phone with a cold "Hello."

In my deepest, sexiest voice I said, "Hello, Melody."

She said, "I have nothing to say to you!" and hung up.

I pressed redial, and when she answered the phone I said, "Melody, it's Clint."

She just shouted, "I told you, I have nothing to say to you!" and hung up again.

I called Tuesday and asked her, "What's up with Melody? She keeps hanging up on me."

Tuesday said, "I don't know what her problem is. She told me she had an amazing time. Maybe that's the problem."

A couple months later I called her again to see how she was doing – and to find out if she was pregnant with "Destiny." She was in a tremendous amount of pain when she answered her cell phone, and I could hear it in her voice.

I said, "What's wrong, Melody?"

She said, "It's that time of the month and I just have to bleed! Stop calling me!" Click.

YOU MUST BOTH BE NAKED

Total nudity is essential to experiencing any of the New Sex techniques in this book.

Nudity is the natural state of humanity, and it's vitally important to be in a natural state in order to be able to access this superpowerful all-natural primal energy.

I had a client call me up once and complain that he was unable to get his girlfriend to ejaculate. I asked him to describe exactly what was going on, and in the process of telling me his experience, he mentioned that he had kept his boxer shorts on when he was in bed with her.

I said, "Think about the tigers in the jungle. When the tigers are having sex, are they wearing boxer shorts? Don't you want to be like a tiger in bed?"

Obviously, he did.

The following week he called me back and said she was gushing like a geyser.

You see, clothing is what separates humans from animals. When you're in pursuit of New Sex Experiences, you need to remove all the barriers that separate you from the primitive state, so that your sex can be raw, natural, and intense.

In that same vein, both partners should remove all jewelry, leather accoutrements, and even makeup.

Ladies, you don't want to slash your man with that big rock on your finger when your arms are flailing about in ecstasy.

You can't expect to make those profound connections when you're hiding behind face masks or face paint either.

You both need to be naked and exposed fully to each other...

Just a naked man in bed with a naked woman...

Pure and natural.

ADEQUATE AROUSAL

While I was busy editing *New Sex Now*, I got a phone call from one of the women to whom I'd sent emails during my quest for a Love Goddess. She was a professional sex surrogate named Dr. Patti Britton.

To make a long story short, I went over to her place one night for a "professional conclave," and after a brutally long and uncomfortable prelude, we got naked and I began the Technique, giving her the Ultimate Erotic Massage exactly as prescribed by Tommy Leonardi, with my extra Clint flourishes thrown in for good measure.

I went through every single step, then got to the part where you put your arm around the woman and receive the RELAXED HUG. I was looking for the SEXY, WAVELIKE MOTION IN HER HIPS, but it wasn't there.

I said (and this is pretty much a direct quote): "Dr. Patti, I'm confused. I've just given you the Ultimate Erotic Massage, and by this point you should be exhibiting a sexy, wavelike motion in your hips as evidence of your arousal."

She said, "It's interesting that you mention that, Clint. As a matter of fact, I'm not very aroused. You see, I have a hard time becoming aroused when I'm only receiving. I need to give as well as receive in order to become really aroused."

So – not because I wanted her to, particularly, but rather, in the interest of science – I allowed Dr. Patti to perform fellatio upon me while I continued to arouse her.

A lot of men are not aware of the powerful impact an erect penis can have on a woman's level of arousal. Women love and get turned on by a hard penis as much as men love and get turned on by the female sex organs.

So if all else fails, and the woman is just not getting aroused, don't be afraid to pull out the "big gun" and remove the safety.

Rub her body with your penis…

Or let her suck on it while you breathe on her vagina or even (when you become more advanced and familiar with G-spot sex) go down on her.

POSITION

The G-spot can be stimulated to orgasm in any position, under any circumstance. Once you get experienced in finding the spot and bringing a woman to climax that way, the only limits are your imagination.

New Sex Advisor #44 © 2001 Clint Arthur & www.NewSex.org
New Sex Techniques Generate Free Sushi & Garage Squirting

I wake up at four in the morning because Cheryl's cell phone is making low-battery beep-beeps.

I stir in bed and try to identify the noise source.

This motion awakens her.

She rustles under the covers and says – straight out of a sound sleep – "I can't believe you made me ejaculate in a parking garage."

* * * * *

It was a very spur-of-the-moment, impromptu date. I had to work late, so I rescheduled an appointment that left my evening open. Although we sleep together almost every night, we're both really busy with our careers and don't get to spend much time together aside from weekends, so it was very exciting for us both to catch a movie and dinner.

The guy in the box office of the Mann six-plex told her, "Every movie in this theater sucks," so it became just dinner.

Sushi at my favorite, Asa Kuma, upstairs, near Barrington.

A couple of Kirin Ichi Bans on tap at the bar while we waited for spots at the sushi bar followed by amazing spicy yellowtail hand rolls, toro tartare with three different colored caviars, scallop sushi, and a spicy tuna cut-up roll. Then I started feeling frisky.

She was wearing a long gray skirt suit and a pink knit top that made her look hugely curvaceous.

All of a sudden my hand slid up under the folds of fabric to trace the lines of her legs...

Up past the knees...

Along the inner thighs...

She flashed her green-gray eyes at me in mock shock at first, then adjusted her legs to give me access.

I was rough with her as I pushed the panties out of my way.

Somehow I was surprised that she was dry...

But I licked my fingers and attempted reinsertion, successfully...

Sliding up along the top wall and making that "come hither" motion with my index and pointer...

Momentarily her natural juices flowed, and she softly moaned, "See what you do to me."

I kept doing it while the waiter brought our check and a busboy refilled water glasses, despite her halfhearted protests that "The hostess is watching us!"

Because I could feel it building in her...

The outrageousness of the situation bolstered the eroticness...

Only about two minutes of this before she's squirming. "Stop it, I'm gonna shoot!"

My hard-on raging... "Go ahead," I say with a laugh – because I'm having such a great time turning her on...

She lets me keep fingering her for another two minutes, but then the movements of my forearm get too obvious and she insists I stop.

"Dinner's on me tonight," she says, slapping down a gold card. "You earned it, you maniac. Now please take me home and fuck me."

[Continued tomorrow.]

Have YOU tried New Sex™ ?

New Sex Advisor #45 © 2001 Clint Arthur & www.NewSex.org
New Sex Techniques Generate Free Sushi & Garage Squirting

I hold my maroon wool jacket in front of my waist to hide the huge, throbbing bulge in my crotch, and we hug each other tight walking out of the sushi restaurant.

Both laughing because everybody in the whole place surely knew that I had been fingering her G-spot for dessert...

Showily licking her juices off my index and pointer, savoring them...

As we stand waiting for the glass elevator, I unzip my fly and set my boner free...

She grabs it with both hands, then bends right over and sucks it in deep.

"What if someone gets out of the elevator?" she asks coming up for a breath.

"Who cares?" I reply full of sex-stoked bravado.

Sure enough, a Mexican restaurant porter shoots right out of the opening doors when the elevator sounds Ding!

Then we get in and she sinks to her knees in the glass-walled people-mover.

When the doors open again on the ground floor she pulls her mouth off me and we start to exit, then I get a bright idea and push "G."

"Where are we going?" she asks, not actually getting it right away.

We stumble out into the subterranean parking lot, and I walk us toward a cinderblock wall in the back...

"Have you been in this garage before?" she asks as I pull up her skirt and bend her over to face and hold onto the secluded side of the wall.

"Never."

My fingers return to her vaginal vault and resume their rhythmic motions.

"That's it!" she pants after around thirty seconds. "That's it, oh my God, you're gonna make me come! Oh my God, I'm gonna squirt right here! I'm gonna squirt!"

Her feet are spread about shoulder-distance apart on $500 Prada fuck-me platforms...

I look down to see muscles cut and ripple her calves as my fingers work her familiar sexual interior like a concert musician plays his instrument...

But the circumstance are so extreme – and our previous experience had always been so classic, in bedrooms, after a relaxing bubble bath, a full body massage, aromatic lotions, candlelight, soft, sensual music – I'm blown away as the ejaculate begins to spray the oil-stained cement floor.

I switch to my thumb and go hitchhiking inside her to produce another spray of liquid between our legs...

The she pleads with me to fuck her, so I yank open my fly and ram inside...

"I'm shooting again! I can feel it on my thighs! I'm gonna soak your pants!"

"Go ahead, soak 'em !" I grunt, pounding away at her slushing snatch.

I don't know how she could let it go under the circumstances – because I certainly couldn't.

I have her turn to suck me a while, then we hear a car engine rev to life close by and decide to repack our equipment before we get caught in the act by a valet.

Sure enough, a black Infinity SUV comes roaring past us as if on cue...

We ride up into the night air on the glass elevator, avoid eye contact with the car parkers, hop in my Bronco, and zoom up the 405 and over the hill.

"You told me once you've been selfish," she says dreamily while I drive. "I can't imagine you ever being a selfish lover."

I think about it and realize how amazing is the power of love – how it brings out the best in us all, especially in me.

I hadn't even shot a load – and I couldn't have cared less.

NOTE: Cheryl was thirty-nine years old when I helped her experience her first female ejaculations, and this little escapade happened just a few months after that blessed event.

I tell you this story not to impress you, but to impress upon you how easy it can become to access the power of the Goddess spot, any time and any place. Even while you're standing with your face pressed up against a brick wall in a parking garage.

New Sex Advisor #42 © 2001 Clint Arthur & www.NewSex.org
Advanced Sex-Tips for Self-Controlled Men & Ejaculating Women

When I'm President of the United States, the weekend will officially end at 1 p.m. on Monday. It's much more civilized that way, almost like a three-day weekend every week, and we can easily make up the lost hours by working just one hour later Monday through Thursday.

Now what does this have to do with sex?

I woke up this morning at 8 a.m., opened my eyes, and saw Cheryl's luscious naked body blur past the bedroom door.

Her huge, double-D curves make waking up on Monday morning an actual joy.

Moments later she came in and sat on the bed wearing a soft pink silk summer dress. My hand slid under the fabric to feel her skin and discover she wasn't wearing any panties.

I remembered that she had an early meeting at her office, so I quickly slid the dress up and entered her every-ready sex with my morning erection. (Normally I wouldn't rush like that, but unfortunately our working world still adheres to such a beastly schedule.)

She self-lubricated almost immediately – our chemistry is so strong.

Pumping into her for many minutes with our legs interlocking like scissors on our sides, then moving into our favorite hot dog, then some missionary madness, then pulling out and fingering her to five female ejaculations before going back inside with my cock and fucking her until she ejaculated on my penis – which spurred me on to my own uncontrollable orgasm – pulling out to shoot a huge splatter of hot cum all over her stomach because she's not on the pill. (She pulled her dress off as I was climaxing, but it got splattered anyway. Sorry, Cheryl!)

The amazing thing was how easily she ejaculated. It happened so quickly! Part of the phenomenon is due to the fact that I've really learned how to get her off with my fingers, and part of it is because she's learned how to access that aspect of her own sexuality more easily as a result of our repeated recent research in that realm.

But also, I realize in retrospect, she had such superfast finger-produced G-spot orgasms because our sexual intercourse had acted like foreplay for the fingering! She gets really turned on when I fuck her, but my fingers can be more effective at stimulating her sacred spot to climax.

So, if you are a man with good self-control and your woman knows how to ejaculate, have sex for a while, then pull out and digitally stimulate her into a series of G-spot orgasms, then go back inside with your penis for that superhot, splashy sex and finish up with an awesome simultaneous ejaculation.

Sincerely,

Your New Sex Advisor

New Sex Advisor #46 © 2001 Clint Arthur & www.NewSex.org
G-spot Mission Accomplished

Here's a letter I got from a man who had the most important thing in the quest to give a woman her first ejaculations: DESIRE!

Hello.

I finally got my wife to ejaculate last night. I've been trying for about three months on a daily basis and twice a day. Finally last night I tried a different approach like I always do, and she said the magic words, she told me she had to pee,...I told her to go for it and wham...a beautiful thing happen....I would like to thank all involved in this group for your inputs, it sure helped a lot, BUT I would like to explain a little further. See, when she was young, a little girl, she had an accident, not to get into detail, but some of her anatomy was removed, it was a little bit of a surprise to me when we first started, but I love her completely so it was a challenge to make her have an orgasm. but I kept trying and after a while you find out what works and what doesn't. Naturally I always tried to make thing interesting, and then I came across your site and read a lot on this subject and finally she came! Again thanks to all and I wish I can return the favor someday somehow.

Tony

Have YOU tried New Sex™ ?

New Sex Advisor #50 © 2001 Clint Arthur & www.NewSex.org
Interview With First-Time Female Ejaculator 10 Minutes After

Cheryl, age 39

Clint: You just experienced your first series of female ejaculations and G-spot orgasms about ten minutes ago. What are your thoughts?

Cheryl: Up until now I'd just felt a glimmer of it – that certain feeling that I didn't know how to identify, but not as intense. It was a chance occurrence, not even something that was recreated. Once or twice, but not for that enduring amount of time, little spurts rather than persistent.

It felt like there was a door that I didn't completely have access to, a side of me that was closed off, but you were more persistent and pushed me to a higher level.

It felt like I was opening up to the other person. I was opening up to you.

It was weird because it felt borderline like I needed to pee, but I knew that wasn't what it was. Almost an uncomfortable feeling, one that penetrates your whole body. Part of you wants it to stop, but part of you doesn't because it feels so great.

It feels like it's really deeper inside your body than a regular orgasm. A regular orgasm is more directional, you feel it in your vaginal area, then it spreads through your body, pulling your whole body in as you're climaxing. It's a greater feeling during the orgasm than normal.

Clint: What were you thinking?

Cheryl: It cleared my mind.

There were little paranoid thoughts about protected sex and where are we going with this? – I'm one who talks in the midst of sex – but when you would hit that point it was like an electric shock that forced my mind to not concentrate.

It takes it down to that rudimentary level – where it should be.

Just very primal.

Just the act, not the thought.

Using your body instead of your mind – which tends to be my problem, I'm too much in my head.

Clint: Describe what it feels like to have your first female ejaculations.

Cheryl: It makes your stomach tense up, and you kind of feel like you have to go to the bathroom, it's not quite right, and you feel like you're on the verge of something, but it's almost uncomfortable because you don't quite know what's happening to you.

So up until today I would feel an edge of it – and I think even released a little bit of amrita – but I was like *I think the other kind of orgasm might be better*. Because it just felt a little more comfortable.

Up until now my stomach and everything would sort of tense up, and I never really completely released. I didn't know that I didn't completely release, so I thought it was sort of tensing my body and I was feeling something, but not as intense as this was.

But when it happens, it really does happen.

You feel like: first your stomach tenses up, and then your whole body tenses up, and then you feel this amazing wash of release.

I can't explain it, but my entire body, from head to toe, is looser. I felt complete release. Like lighter. Like I've let go of something.

But it's completely different from being on the verge of having it happen. That was a completely different experience.

And it IS about letting go. I was holding onto it, so I wasn't letting myself go with it, so there's a point of climax that's almost borderline uncomfortable and can stay uncomfortable (not in a really bad way, but uncomfortable), like you have to go to the bathroom, and your body is tense, and if you don't go through it then you can't completely release and it isn't as positive an experience.

I was holding onto that, not getting over the edge – which is a really intense part. It's almost like just as you're about to climax in a regular orgasm, and your whole body is all tense – like if you stop, your body goes insane! ... and that's where I'd been all along – and then finally just letting go of it gets you up and over that factor, to complete release. And that's WOW! So different! My body feels different.

New Sex Advisor #51 © 2001 Clint Arthur & www.NewSex.org
"How to Let Go"

Clint: What was it that enabled you to let go?

Cheryl: In my head, I just kinda listened to the music and was more here and now, present – didn't think, just did – let my body feel open and just do it.

Clint: Did you have to do anything to your body?

Cheryl: No, just relax it. Because the problem is when you start to feel it get tense, then you tense up more, and then you can't let go of something. So instead, you relax.

When I was on the verge of that I was tensing up, and it wouldn't let me go past it. So this time I just sort of lay and listened to the music and relaxed my body, and it did what I guess it's supposed to do. Wow!

Clint: What about when it was going on – what was it like when it was happening?

Cheryl: My entire stomach kind of tensed up. Then I felt my whole vaginal area, uterus, everything just sort of release.

And each time I did it, it was easier. Because my body understood it.

First I was tense because I didn't know what was going on, then I relaxed more into it and more into it, and then the last time it just naturally happened. There wasn't that tension. So it makes me think that when your body doesn't know what's going on there is tension, but the last time it happened, when you were inside me, my body was relaxed and I didn't go through that tense period, it just released.

That tension, that uncomfortableness, is only brought on by your own body not relaxing into it. Because once it happened and happened again, my body was like "Whoa!" And just having you inside of me, it just let go of it naturally, and the tension I was feeling initially just wasn't even there. It was just release, and that tingling feeling.

Clint: What about the last one?

Cheryl: While you were inside of me? My body had done it a couple of times, so not only could I relax into it, but then I felt you inside of me, and then I felt you starting to come inside of me, and it was really warm, and that just sort of pushed me to the next level and made me release at the same time. I was reacting to your body.

Clint: I came so fast with you – you were like electricity. And usually I have a lot of control and staying power, but it was so exciting and hot – Mmmmm! You felt so free and natural.

Cheryl: It feels like you broke through a wall.

Clint: What do you mean?

Cheryl: It felt like you were deeper and more intense. It felt like it's a part of me. The two of us were part of one particular act. It wasn't separate. It wasn't action and reaction – it was all simultaneously happening.

Clint: You mean when we were having sex it was more unified than normal?

Cheryl: Yeah. Once I stopped fighting it and finally let go.

Clint: Why do you think you were fighting it?

Cheryl: It wasn't even a conscious mental effort. My body didn't know what was going on. It wasn't deciphering the sensations. You had once said that the G-spot is so close to your bladder that your body thinks that you have to go to the bathroom.

But the funny thing is that the first time we started doing this, I did feel like I had to go to the bathroom. It was because my body was so tense that it was sort of blurring the senses of all those organs together.

When I relaxed into it, it was such a separate, different feeling than that feeling of having to go to the bathroom.

It was completely different from the way it was a week ago. Because I was tensing my body, so all those organs were coming together and I couldn't decipher the different feelings.

Relaxing my body allowed me to relax into it, and it didn't feel like I really had to go to the bathroom. It was that intensity, but in a good way.

It's funny, because I think once it happens, it's completely different.

I completely let go of it, and it's a completely different feeling.

And once it happens for you, you realize what's happening to your body, and I think it's easier to let go of it again and again. Because first you're thinking that your body is doing something unnatural, so you tense it up. But if you just relax into it, and the person you're with knows what they're doing, it just happens.

Clint: What about your past experiences in this realm of sexuality?

Cheryl: About five years ago my boyfriend (at the time) and I took Charles and Carolyn Muir's seminar, and we learned about the sacred spot and amrita. We tried the techniques and everything that they told us to do, but weren't able to achieve this. I just figured I wasn't able to do it. And they never came right out and said, "Every woman can ejaculate," the way you do. So my boyfriend and I tried, and just didn't get very far. Maybe I got somewhere close to the edge, but I never got to the edge, and certainly never got over the edge.

Clint: Why not?

Cheryl: I think it's because he didn't know what to do exactly, the way you do. And he wasn't persistent enough. They gave us a general idea of what kind of stuff would go on, but nobody ever said do this and this and this, and this, that, and the other thing will happen...

Clint: Like I do on "New Sex Now"...

Cheryl: We just tried, and when I couldn't do it, gave up. I was left feeling like it was my fault, that I wasn't able to do it.

Clint: That's too bad, because every woman is physically capable of ejaculating and enjoying sacred spot, a.k.a. G-spot, orgasms. It's too bad for you he didn't have the step-by-step New Sex™ Techniques telling him exactly what to do. But then, his loss is my gain.

Have YOU tried New Sex™?

New Sex Advisor #27 © 2001 Clint Arthur & www.NewSex.org
The Time-Sex Continuum

It is a Sunday morning, and lying beside me in her big fluffy bed, my luscious Cheryl.

She is naked.

Blonde sleep-tousled hair partially obscures her beautiful face, but through the sandy locks full lips offer a faint smile in the relaxed ease of sleep…

Thoughts of many pleasures given by those lips provides the impetus…

I dive under the covers, careful not to disturb her slumber…

Admiring silky tan flesh of thighs…

Close-trimmed hairs above and tracing lips of her love temple.

Ever so gently I lay my tongue on the topmost part of her labia…

Taste the first salts of her sex…

Just hold it there a long while…

Notice she does not stir from dreamtime as saliva builds in my mouth…

Softly I suck on her clit…

Lips kiss tender mound…

Tongue nudges blood to flow…

And it awakens as she herself begins to stir…

Gives a little gasp…

Rubs sleep from her eyes.

A lazy half-turn of her torso, and legs spread to allow me fuller access…

Now I feast on the delights of her sex, open to me, receptive…

Encouraging…

Hips respond with subtle waves…

Juices…

Mmmmm, the taste of heaven…

Clean and fresh and quick to come…

Natural chemistry between us…

With legs near her head, I feel hair brush my thigh, then the hot, sweet wet of her tongue takes a first lick…

And she sucks me in soft against her lips…

Her mouth enlivens my wand of light…

Only moments pass before my blood courses into sexual channels to make it full…

Full of loving energy for her…

And I shift my body up on the bed…

While at the same time I pull her down…

More onto my face…

Those yummy woman's hips…

Bending back her right leg out of the way to open her…

Spreading wide the vault…

I look at liquid glisten in morning sunlight…

Lap it up…

While she sucks – oh how she sucks me!

Deep, wet, and full of desire…

To the root…

Urging rock hardness…

Sucks and nibbles and carnal licks…

We live it up and feel it up, and for a brief moment I even raise it up to thank God for this woman, this body, this richness.

I cannot fairly judge the span of time we enjoy as thus…

With no goals other than immersion in feelings of love, an essential shift takes hold of my mind and being…

We revert to instinct and animal purity in the bedroom…

I do not care about anything now, beside the pleasure…

No place else, no one else, nothing else…

Together we transcend social constraints in a tangle of writhing limbs…

We float on clouds of passion…
Up above the fracas…
Through the jet stream…
Up, up, up to a place where we are untouchable…
Safe and soaring in the sacred Time-Sex Continuum.

REVIEW QUIZ

1. According to Clint Arthur, Goddess Mare Simone, and Dr. Corynna Clarke, _____ women can ejaculate.

2. The key to great cunnilingus is to suck and stimulate a woman's clitoris as if it were a miniature _____.

3. The creases behind a woman's _____ are a very sexy place to lick and suck.

4. _____ on a woman's vagina for a LONG TIME to drive her absolutely out of her mind.

5. A subtle but powerful tool for arousing a woman is for the man to grind his _____ _____into the crack of her butt while massaging her back.

6. Swooshing your fingers around the _____, deep inside the vaginal vault, is another powerful arousal technique.

7. The essential key to sensual lovemaking mastery is maximizing the level of your _____ _____.

8. Describe the "Switching-Out" Technique.

9. After simultaneous ejaculations, the man's orgasm will continue as long as the man's penis remains _____ ____ _____ vagina.

3
HIS ULTIMATE PLEASURE

MALE MULTIPLE "MORE-GASMS"

Beth and the baby came back East with me for my grandmother's funeral, and there was one highlight of that terrible time:

I was feeling very frisky the night after the funeral, and when I started to come on to Beth she said, "You know, Clint, when people die, that's when people can get pregnant really easily, so we better be extra careful – we don't want to have another baby."

I said, "I agree."

Then she said, "Maybe this would be a good time to try out that Ultimate Blowjob Theory you told me about."

I said, "What a great idea!"

The Ultimate Blowjob Theory came to me in a flash on the first afternoon when I was writing the book with Tommy. He was playing testimonial tapes of women he'd been with, and one of them said, "You have to let go and go over the wall to the Ultimate Orgasm."

As soon as I heard that, my mind flashed back to a time that I was in Dallas when I was twenty-five years old. I'd met a beautiful and extremely sexy blonde at the mall, and the mutual attraction between us was BLATANTLY OBVIOUS to us both.

We went out that night and ended up parked by a lake in her Mustang.

She wouldn't let me have sex with her in the car because that was "trashy."

We couldn't go back to her place because she lived with her brother…

And I had already checked out of my hotel…

So there we were, a couple of frustrated, horny kids on a hot night.

REVIEW QUIZ

1. Swallowing is not about _____. It's about
   _____ everything about your lover.

2. When pursuing the Ultimate Male Orgasm, the man must
   force himself to let the woman keep _____ ___ _____.

3. Both men and women can have multiple _____ and
   multiple _____.

4. The five psychological aspects of male multiple
   ejaculation are T_____, R_____, D_____, N_____,
   and P_____ ___ ____ _____.

5. In order for a man to experience multiple ejaculations, he
   must be willing to be _____ and out of _____.

4
RAW POWER

MY RUSSIAN GODDESS

In August I got an email from the Goddess Natalia replying to an email I'd sent her back in June inviting her over to the boat shortly after meeting her at Anthea's love temple.

I emailed her my number, and she called me at around 9:30 p.m., while I was changing into my workout gear at the gym. It was a warm night, and I asked if she wanted to take a drive up the coast in my convertible 1971 Bronco after I got done working out. She said that sounded like fun, and that I should pick her up at midnight.

She came out of her apartment building looking a bit reserved. After all, it had been quite a while since we'd met that night at the ejaculation ceremony. Things were a tad uncomfortable until we started cruising up the Pacific Coast Highway, and then the magic of the evening began to set in.

A midnight rendezvous, two bottles of Mango Madness, a large assortment of extra-fancy grapes, a Russian tantra Goddess, a classic convertible, and a warm summer night along the PCH make a recipe for something truly beautiful.

I steered us up onto Big Rock Road, wanting to find a nice vista point to park and make out. Up and up and up we went, until very near the top I pulled over at a house under construction where the temporary chainlink fence permitted us a partial view of the Queen's Necklace lights sparkling along Santa Monica Bay.

We got out and ate grapes off the hood of my Bronco, admiring the full moon and billions of sparkling stars in the black night sky. I told her about the vampire movie I had written and was going to star in, which was starting production in a few weeks. Then I started to suck on her neck.

She said, "The vampire is sucking on my neck under a full moon!"

I said, "I'm not the vampire, I'm the hero. I kill the vampire."

Then I noticed that the construction fence was standing slightly ajar, and that we could slip through and go down to explore the house below on the hillside. She was wary at first, but I led her down the steps toward the magnificent multimillion-dollar Malibu manse, and right in through the open space where the front door had yet to be installed.

We were immediately transported to another level as the living room windows offered up their panoramic "Jet Liner Views" of the entire coast. Being in this house made you feel like you'd arrived, even while it was under construction. But the windows did not open, and it was a little stuffy inside, so I led us out a patio door to the flat grassy hillside.

We stood there breathing in the hot Santa Ana breezes, basking in the moonlight, awed by the spectacular vista before us...

Hugging her from behind, with my chin just above her shoulder, I massaged her neck and skull with my hands as I softly breathed on and began to suck the milky white skin above her throat muscles.

Unbuttoning her blouse, I was amazed to find her large 36D breasts unconstrained by any bra, just hanging free and available to my touch.

We stood there tingling with erotic energy as I cupped her breasts in my hands and lightly teased the nipples with my fingertips.

It was such a warm night, and we were delirious with sensory pleasure when I took off my shirt and cuddled up behind her to engage our flesh connection.

We stood like that for a long while, then I unbuttoned her jeans and slid them off her hips and down around her ankles. She stepped out of her pants and immediately turned to unbutton mine.

My hard-on popped straight out, and she dropped to her knees and immediately began sucking.

Wow! To be standing on that cliff, with the hot, sultry mouth of my long-lusted-for Russian Goddess wrapped around my raging manhood – what a rush!

How far I had come since beginning this New Sex Now phase of my life!

After she pleasured me orally for a long while, I guided her to stand and face the huge pane-glass behind us, arched her back, dropped to my knees, and brought my mouth up under her yoni to lick and suck and lavish her with pleasure for a brief eternity of delicious indulgence…

I caught the view out of my peripheral vision, and the sight of her GORGEOUS naked breasts and beautiful face reflected on the glass in front of all the sparkling lights of the coast was UNBELIEVABLE!

Then, when she was searing hot, I stood up and turned her head with my left hand so that I could kiss her mouth and look in her eyes while I slowly guided my penis inside her from behind.

She was spread wide, perfectly angled, fully lubricated, and completely inviting…

There was no thinking, only being.

Hot breaths of passion…

Deep, full dancing tongues…

A crush of naked flesh and perfectly proportioned bodies…

Bending knees…

And thrusting hips…

Handfuls of perfect pendulous breasts…

Blonde hair, sparkling lights, and the full moon…

Fucking like that against the glass for over an hour…

Then going inside and reversing the angle, now looking directly out at the view instead of the reflection, and continuing this epic showing for another forty minutes of naked pounding…

It was SO INCREDIBLE.

I thought about not coming…

But eventually I decided that I had to come. I deserved to come. And I was going to come inside her.

So there I was, hard and deep inside one of the hottest female specimens ever, totally in control, in no hurry at all, having performed at a world-class level, totally unselfishly…

I said, "I'm gonna cum."

She said, "Yes, baby, yes!"

••

So began my beautiful love affair with Goddess Natalia.

It was like playing tennis with a great tennis player – my "game" was in its utmost form.

In the beginning I would come over to her place late at night, we would hang out in her living room listening to KCRW, smoke a few hits of pot, and get very sexy on a new drug she introduced me to called GHB.

This high was like the very best love element of Ecstasy and the sexiest buzz of being drunk combined together in a very erotic mix.

I remember the first time at her house, she had an automatic CD changer, and we made love for three entire Sade albums.

Never once did I verge on accidentally coming.

I was always perfectly controlled, because I didn't want to cum…

I didn't want the experience to end.

PRESENCE IN THE MOMENT

The third night I spent at Goddess Natalia's was another marathon of groovy tunes and supersensuality, a few hits of her good buds and a shot of the magical GHB cocktail.

While we were making love on her living room futon she said, "Every time we make love, it's always so different!"

The only thing I can attribute that to is total and complete Presence in the Moment…

<u>Complete awareness of what is going on...</u>
<u>Complete attention on interacting with the other person...</u>
<u>Completely Being Here Now.</u>
<u>Completely NOT being in my head.</u>

When I was in my late twenties I studied at the Howard Fine Acting Studio, one of the top acting schools in Hollywood, with Howard Fine himself. He's the one who taught us the phrase "Getting stuck in your head."

Basically, it means that you're busy thinking about what you're doing, rather than actually doing it.

The trick he taught us for how to get "unstuck" and "out of your head" is to use your senses.

LOOK...

LISTEN...

TOUCH...

SMELL...

FEEL...

Movie stars like Nicholas Cage and Robert De Niro get paid millions of dollars to be up there on the silver screen because the way they act makes them seem "larger than life."

What makes them appear larger than life is the fact that they are living more actively than the average person.

<u>They are using their senses more actively...</u>

As a result, they are "more alive" than regular folks.

When Goddess Natalia was commenting on the high quality of our sex, what she was responding to was simply the fact that I was COMPLETELY NOT IN MY HEAD when I was with her...

I was totally ON...

Totally PRESENT.

Totally BEING...

Not thinking...

Living in the moment.

You have to use this same technique to make sure that you and your lover remain PRESENT IN THE MOMENT at all times during lovemaking.

Look at your lover's EYEBALLS...

Check out her LASHES...

Really SEE her PUBIC HAIR...

Touch her SILKY SKIN...

Her earlobes...

The softness of her hair...

The bed sheets...

Taste the SALTINESS of her sweat...

Or her natural juices...

The flavor of the wine...

An Altoid...

The edible panties...

Listen to her HEARTBEAT...

Get into the MUSIC...

The rhythm of her breathing...

The squeaking of the bed frame...

The couple in the next room...

Smell the fragrance of sex in the air...

The flowers... The incense... The air.

COUNT THE STROKES

A great lovemaking technique is for the man to count the number of thrusts or strokes he makes inside the woman's yoni temple. According to ancient wisdom, a good man should make no less than one hundred strokes.

Goddess Natalia inspired me to do sets of five hundred.

Set after set after set...

Enjoying the workout!

Not really showing off my control – because it wasn't about showing off; it was about sharing pleasure...

A meeting of two specially connected sexual souls dancing a sacred sex lovers' tango.

In that context, the concept of having a quick orgasm was simply not acceptable – and quite frankly, never entered my mind.

I wanted to be every bit as good as ANY lover she had ever been with.

And with that goal in mind, I specifically stayed away from her Goddess spot for several weeks as we got to know and grow comfortable with each other.

In fact, I didn't even touch her G-spot again until one night when we were invited over to the home of Dr. Corynna Clarke for a little sex party.

I got to Natalia's house some time after 10 p.m., and she asked, "Would you like to go over to a little party at Corynna's?"

"You mean Dr. Corynna Clarke? What kind of party?"

"Who knows with those tantra people. Probably some kind of orgy. I don't know."

I said, "Sure. If you want to go."

She said, "It would be good for me to go, because of business. Corynna's website makes me a lot of money. But we don't have to go."

I said, "I'd love to go."

"Okay, you're a grown man, and you'll do what you want to do, which is fine with me, but here are some condoms, and I think you should wear them if you're with anyone else. Those tantra people are not always so perfectly clean. And some of them have diseases."

I said, "Are you perfectly clean?"

She said, "Until I was with you I was. Have you given me any diseases, Clint?"

"As a matter of fact I went and got checked recently, and the doctor at the clinic said I was clear." I always went to STD clinics in "The Hood" to get VD screening at periodic six-month intervals, and had gone just recently.

On the drive over to Corynna's, I asked Natalia if she was worried about getting pregnant and she said it "couldn't happen. It's impossible." She never elucidated on that, even though I inquired a few times during our time together.

Natalia was a beautiful, tall, busty, sexy woman, and always looked great. That night she wore a low-cut velvet dress that flattered her cleavage to maximum effect. So much so that when we entered Corynna's apartment, Dr. Clarke, her boyfriend Evan, and Goddess Anthea all gasped "Wow!" at first sight of her, and even started applauding!

As I had feared, my date was the hottest chick at the party. When we left about an hour after arriving, we went back to Natalia's place and made love, and I was so relieved that no one else got to lay a finger on her.

"BEDTIME STORIES"

At that point in my life I had terrible credit. So once I finished editing *New Sex Now*, I signed up for a website and got my mother to set up a credit-card merchant account for me through her corporation.

My mother was selling my explicit sex video for me!

I then set about the task of letting the world know about the amazing New Sex Experience.

Now, you'd probably expect that selling a new sex experience would be easy! Lo and behold, you'd be wrong.

Our society is very jaded about pornography making its way into mainstream media. You can use sex to sell cars, cosmetics, and candy... But don't try to use sex to sell sex – people don't like that.

It took me months of work banging my head up against the mainstream media wall before I finally go a break, connecting with gonzo porn legend Ed Powers, who also hosted a radio program on 97.1 KLSX, L.A.'s number-one talk-radio station.

Ed was generous enough to invite me onto his show to talk about New Sex and female ejaculation – on the condition that I bring a girl with me to talk about it too.

I called Dr. Corynna Clarke and asked her if she would be interested. Her only condition was that she wouldn't allow him to ask her any questions about her cup size. She felt that was degrading to women.

So that Saturday night I took off from my job driving a hack, dressed up in my sexy Armani X shirt, and picked up Dr. Corynna Clarke at her apartment shortly after 10:30 p.m.

We drove down to the radio station's studio on Wilshire Boulevard near Normandy, and had the greatest time talking with Ed Powers and his millions of listeners about the wonders of female ejaculation, G-spot orgasms, amrita, the Goddess spot, sacred sexuality, and my video *New Sex Now*.

Ed was kind enough to let us plug our websites a bunch of times during the four hours we spent with him, and I got to repeat my favorite line over and over: "Women, if you can hear the sound of my voice, you can ejaculate."

And Dr. Clarke backed up everything I said!

BRIGIT THE MIDGET'S G-SPOT

Ed Powers had a regular guest on his show by the name of Brigit Powerz. She was a three-foot-tall porn star, a beautiful woman in a pint-size body.

Brigit was also a guest the night that we appeared on "Bedtime Stories," and she admitted on the air that she had never experienced a G-spot orgasm or female ejaculation. Corynna and I described exactly where the G-spot was and what she could do to herself to have the experience.

The following weekend I was listening to the show on the radio and called in to say hi. Brigit was a guest in the studio again, and as soon as she heard my voice she said, "Oh my God, Clint! I did it! Last week I went home after the show and found my G-spot and learned how to squirt! I did it! It was amazing! And the only reason I could do it was because you said I could!"

Many women are able to find their G-spot and learn how to ejaculate simply by becoming aware of their natural ability.

Enlightenment is power!

So, ladies, if you are reading these words, you have a G-spot and are fully capable of enjoying the intense pleasures of female ejaculations and multiple G-spot orgasms.

A MINISCULE PERCENTAGE OF WOMEN CAN'T

Having just made that blanket statement immediately above, let me now state that there exists a miniscule percentage of women who do not have a G-spot and cannot ejaculate.

These women have actually had their G-spot removed by surgical operation.

In the early part of the twentieth century, some women would go to their gynecologist and complain of embarrassing "incontinence" during sexual intercourse with their husbands.

Regrettably for them, the only surefire method for "curing" this "embarrassing problem" was the surgical removal of their G-spot.

That took care of the problem!

I feel sad for those women, and hope that this work will prevent further needless embarrassment and sexual mutilations.

SENSUAL FEASTING

During the vampire movie production, I injured my knees pretty badly when I jumped and a swell surged the ship's deck..

I sought help from my chiropractor, Stuart Hoffman, and that's when I first got introduced to the Raw Food Primal Diet.

Basically, people on this diet only eat raw food, with the belief that the nutrients in the food are enough to heal any illness when taken in the right combinations.

We looked in a book of remedies that Stuart had, and I saw a diagnosis for "Weak Knees: If you feel like your knees are weak, or that your legs will give out underneath your own body weight, you have a deficiency in the thyroid gland, and should eat an abundance of raw shellfish, including raw clams, oysters, and scallops."

Raw clams and oysters had been my favorite foods for a long time, but I rarely ate them because of the expense involved. But now they were a key part of my cure, so I went to town at the raw bar, and made up for lost time.

Now everyone knows the old saying about eating raw oysters and sex. But after Natalia and I started feasting on oysters together at her house prior to every lovemaking session, she said to me, "My God, it's like STEEL!"

It was true. It must have something to do with absorbing the natural life force and vitality of the freshly killed animal.

All I know is, after a few short months of eating oysters every day, my knees were back to normal strength, and my steel rod was stronger than ever.

And every time I've ever begun a romantic interlude with appetizers of raw oysters and/or clams on the half-shell, the scene has always been set for a great night of passion and sensual power.

Another key reason to eat raw oysters and clams prior to sharing a sacred sexuality experience with someone is the concept of sacrifice.

Religious ceremonies have begun with a sacrifice since time immemorial. By sacrificing the lives of a dozen oysters or clams to the honor of God or your Higher Power, you are adding the ritual element of sacrifice to your sacred sex experience.

THE ULTIMATE FORCE: DESIRE

I had been seeing the Goddess Natalia once or twice a week for over three months before I was able to satisfy the psychological factors required for her to really let go with me and let it flow.

It was very frustrating, because here I was supposed to be this "expert" on the G-spot and female ejaculation, and yet I had been unable to satisfy the Goddess the way I knew she needed to be satisfied.

This professional tantra Goddess was a special case for me, since I knew that almost all strippers, porn actresses, and "sex-industry workers" have some sort of psychosexual issue that got them into sex work in the first place, so I didn't get down on myself over how long it was taking.

I just kept focusing on the fact that I wanted to give her pleasure. Until I finally got her (and us) where I wanted to take us: up and over the wall. I knew that I was going to keep doing my best, and keep doing everything I knew that needed to be done to bring her to the heights of female pleasure.

There was never the fear that I wouldn't some day be able to succeed. My desire kept the goal realistic and crystal clear.

That's not to say that giving her G-spot orgasms was the only reason I was with her. It wasn't. I was with Goddess Natalia because she was fun to be with, she was present with me at all times, we were into each other, we had great chemistry, she was sympathetic to my goals and ambitions, and I had a great desire to know her physically and emotionally.

We were lying in her bed one night, watching *The Nanny*, which was the only TV show we ever watched. We had smoked some pot and taken just the right amount of GHB.

When Fran Drescher had laughed her final, ridiculous laugh, I undressed the Goddess, SLOWLY AND GENTLY, kissing and softly rubbing her entire body from head to toe...

BREATHING ON HER NIPPLES...

Breathing on her yoni, <u>but not touching it</u>…

Then spreading her legs and crawling up so my face was right there, close to her tight-trimmed yoni…

Just breathing and panting hot breaths into it…

Inhaling the fresh aroma…

Then I started going down on her…

After about ten minutes of that, I moved my hips so we formed a 69…

And we stayed in that heavenly position for a long time just enjoying the closeness of it, the intimacy of being naked and sucking and licking and slurping another naked being whom you are into.

Then I turned over so I was lying side by side with her…

<u>I put my left arm around her shoulder and held her strongly in my embrace…</u>

<u>I kissed her with sincere passion and love…</u>

Then I gently slid two fingers inside her yoni temple…

And started slowly swooshing around her cervix…

Pressing and releasing her sacred spot, with a gentle, building rhythm…

She was responding, yet nowhere near letting go…

So I kept going and going and going…

She kept building and building…

It was getting more and more intense…

And then somehow, through some divine inspiration, I slid my hips underneath her butt…

And slid my *lingam* (penis) inside her temple at the same time that I was fingering her…

It was such a tight fit with my fingers and my penis shoved inside…

And it was SOOOOOO HOTTTTT!

Suddenly I felt her going CRAZY!!!!!

Breathing in passionate out-of-control gasps in a way I'd never heard from her before…

Her entire pelvic region pulsing and thrusting so wildly that it took a lot of wrestling strength and agility for me to keep control of her body…

But my natural mating instincts assured that I did whatever had to be done to keep my cock inside her, thrusting, pumping, building up a hot load of shooting semen-seed…

And then in a rush of saliva-swapping tongues, sweaty-skin-sliding, and thump-crushing pelvic thrusts, all at once, from somewhere deep within the furthest depths of the Goddess came a long-awaited explosion of searing hot amrita.

The intensity of this moment was WAY BEYOND MY CONTROL…

I was powerless to try and resist…

The SWITCH WAS FLICKED…

The CURRENT WAS ON…

The Great Goddess was flowing upon me…

And *B-O-O-M-!* – I instantly shot my seed into the flow.

I was GROWLING!

And she was W-A-I-L-I-N-G AND MOANING and S-C-R-E-A-M-I-N-G with exhilarated pleasure…

We were drenched in sweat…

Muscles taut…

Hearts racing…

Blood RUSHING through our veins…

Total intensity!!!

I said, "Thank you, my Goddess."

She said, "Thank you, my God…"

And thereupon, we both passed out.

GODDESS NATALIA'S FIRST AMRITA

The next day, over breakfast, Goddess Natalia told me the true story of how she first learned to experience amrita.

"A few years ago," she said, handing me a cup of coffee and sitting down beside me on her black leather couch, "about a year after my divorce, I read about a seminar given by a husband and wife named Charles and Caroline Muir.

"I did some investigating about them, and I found out that they gave very respectful, very safe seminars, and I enrolled to take a weekend course here in Los Angeles.

"It was given at the Sheraton Miramar Hotel in Santa Monica. President Bill Clinton used to stay in that same hotel when he came to Los Angeles.

"It was a two-day seminar, and we all knew that at the end of the first night, the people who didn't come with partners to the seminar would be given the opportunity to pair up to do the special homework assignment, which would be focusing on the woman's pleasure, in a special ceremony, which would hopefully result in the experience of amrita.

"Charles and Caroline were so charming, and disarming, that they made the entire experience completely nonthreatening. They had big stuffed-animal-like lingam and yoni puppets, which they used in acting out the whole experience of sex, and everything was very light and fun.

"So that day when it came time to break for lunch, a whole group of us went out to a restaurant on Third Street Promenade. And in the group were several men and several single women, and the whole time I knew that everyone was jockeying for position to see who was going to be paired up with whom that night.

"There was one man there who was very tall, with dark hair and dark skin – he was Brazilian, a Jewish man — and I just knew that I wanted to be paired up with him. I wanted to ask him to be my partner after lunch while we were walking back to the hotel, but there were two other women who also wanted him, and as we were all walking back together there was never a moment when I could be alone with him.

"So the afternoon became the night, and all the men split off into one group to be prepared by Charles Muir for this special ceremony, only focusing on the woman's pleasure, telling them what to expect, and what to do, how to set the mood and stay focused on the woman, and keep from putting the attention on themselves.

"And Caroline took all the women into one group, separate from the men, and she told us what it would be like, and that women normally in our culture are trained to focus on the man's pleasure, but that tonight it would be a special ceremony only for our pleasure, and that no matter how much we felt a natural inner compulsion to please the man, we were forbidden to even touch him! This was only about us! We had to fight with our own selves to make sure we fulfilled our responsibility to the ceremony, and only received pleasure.

"It sounds funny, but you know, Clint, it's true. Women feel a tremendous inner pressure to please men. It's not easy to just receive. But Caroline told us that we had to – just receive.

"So the way they organized it was this: First they said that anyone who didn't want to participate could leave. This homework assignment was purely voluntary, and no one had to do it. So first they asked if any men wanted to leave, and of course all the men stayed!" We both laughed.

"Then they asked if any of the women wanted to leave, and there were a few timid souls who just couldn't bring themselves to participate in this type of thing with someone they really didn't know. I mean, we all had been together the entire day in the seminar, and at lunch, but really, what did we know about these men? Nothing!

"So the ones who wanted to leave left, and then there were the women who stayed, and of course too many men. So they said that all of the men were going to sit in the middle of the room and close their eyes, and then the women would get to choose who they wanted to be with.

"I felt so sorry for some of those men, because they all knew that they were volunteering just to give pleasure in this beautiful ceremony to whichever women selected them, and some of them were not going to be chosen. They were so brave, those men. There was one who was so old, it was almost certain he wouldn't be chosen, but he stayed, and I felt so bad for him when he opened his eyes and no one had picked him.

"So it came time for the moment when all the women would choose, and a few of the women at lunch were there too, and I knew that more than one of us wanted that same guy, so when they said, 'Ready, set, go!' I fucking RAN over to that guy and hugged him! And when he opened his eyes and saw it was me he was smiling SO BIG!"

I said, "I'm sure he was."

"And some of those other women were SO PISSED, because he was definitely the hottest guy.

"So they said we could go to a hotel, or whatever arrangements we wanted, and he offered for us to use his place up in the Hollywood Hills.

"We drove up there and he told me that he was a rabbi. And a musician – a drummer. So when we arrived he put some really cool, very sensual Latin American drumming music on the stereo, and he prepared a bath and lit candles and incense. Charles had really prepared them very well, because there was never any hint of him wanting me to touch him or do anything for him. This was just about me, about my pleasure. It was the first time I ever had any experience like that in my life.

"That night he gave me his total devotion. And that was my first experience of amrita. After that, I was never able to do it with another person, only by myself. Until last night."

I looked into her eyes and savored the moment of connection and intimacy that had developed between us and crystallized at that point in time. Then I asked, "Why?"

"I knew deep inside that I was safe, and I could trust you."

REVIEW QUIZ

1. One of the most powerful methods for being a great lover is to be fully _____ in the _____.

2. Movie stars appear to be "more alive than regular people" because they are using their _____ more actively.

3. List nine things you can do to be more present with your lover (or anyone at any time):

4. Many women learn how to ejaculate immediately after they become _____ that they can.

5. Eating raw _____ and _____ will imbue you with powerful life-force energy and add a _____ element of sacrifice to your Sacred Sex experience.

6. _____ will make any goal realistic, any outcome crystal clear.

7. For women, it is not always easy only to _____ pleasure.

8. When attempting to share female ejaculations with a woman for the first time, a man should stay focused on the woman's _____.

9. What is the meaning of the term "Count the strokes"?

5
AURAL SEX

MASTER SEX TALK

I go to a lot of adult webmaster conventions in Las Vegas and around the country to promote www.NewSex.org and to learn about the latest advances on the Internet. At a shmooze-fest during Adultdex last year, I had a very important conversation with a webmistress who had bought our instructional video *New Sex Now*.

Her name was Sharon, and she owns a number of very cool adult sites, among them: www.AgeOldPussy.com sexyoldsluts.com, fatfanny.com, and BigandSexy.com. She's a very cool ex-hippie swinger from Michigan, who's been just about everywhere and done just about everything with (I presume) just about everybody – so I really took what she had to say very seriously as we sipped cocktails at a high-up hospitality suite in the Tropicana Hotel.

"I watched your video, Clint," she said. "And I gotta tell ya, hon, I really liked it a lot. In fact, I had my husband watch it. Not that he needed to learn anything – because he's super in bed – but it was a good refresher for him. To remind him about certain things."

"Thank you," I said, genuinely honored.

"The only thing is, I think you should have done more about aural sex."

"You mean sex talk?"

"It's <u>SO</u> important to talk during sex. If my husband doesn't talk to me during sex, I'm liable to start thinking about work and my website statistics – and that's not good."

"I know!" On *New Sex Now* there's a whole section devoted specifically to the importance of being present in the moment during sex. "So what do you want a man to say during sex?"

"Oh anything!" she said, getting very animated. "Tell me about what you're doing to me, or what you're gonna do to me, or what you wish you could do to me with the monkey.... Anything, just to keep me from getting distracted."

She had an amazing point. As we all should know, the most powerful erogenous zone in the body is located between our ears.

Talking to your partner during sex not only activates an important sensory organ (your ears) but also activates your mind. When done properly, your sex talk can have a tremendous impact on the erotic power of a sexual encounter.

The importance of this issue prompted me to record an audio CD entitled *Master Sex Talk*, which focuses on this key technique. Following is the transcript of sex dialogue taken from the actual lovemaking session used on that recording. Feel free to borrow any dialogue, or use it as a springboard for your own sex talk.

●●

"It's so deep inside me...
"Every inch of you...
"It almost hurts – and then you just go so much deeper...
"What you do to me...
""
"When we were dancing at the club tonight, I wanted so much to be fucking you...
"It feels like you're sucking my balls inside you..."
"Your balls are just hitting my clit!
"I wanted you inside me at the club!"
"I wanted you to be blowing me at the club!
"I wanted you to be sucking me at the club!
"The saxophone player was smiling at me because you were so fucking hot and sexy tonight."
"Walking down the street tonight, I wanted to feel you inside of me.
"Pump it in me!"

"Open your legs, and let me in!"

"Oh God, it's so deep!

"It's so sensitive tonight – it's so deep inside of me!"

"I feel like my balls are inside you."

"I want every inch of you."

"Every inch is all yours.

"Throw your legs open!

"I love feeling your naked flesh around my cock."

"Just take me!

"Anything you want.

"Just take me, fuck me!"

"Oh yeah – throw your legs open like that – wide – just take me in!"

"Shove it in me!"

"I felt it hitting your cervix."

"No one's ever been there – it seems like everything you do is different."

"Yeah, suck my cock with your pussy!

"Suck that cock!"

"Just slam it against me – pound me with your cock!"

"I love when you're open!

"Oh, you're so wet!"

"I just want to throw my legs in the air and just fuck you!

"Take me, it's all yours!"

"No one else, baby, no one else – just you!

"I'll never stop fucking you!"

"God, when you shove it in me so deep – it's so tight up against me!"

"Come on my cock!"

"Oh fuck me!

"Oh God, it feels like it's a part of me – like it's a piece of me!"

"I feel like I'm gonna rip you open!

"I've never had a woman open up to me like you!

"*You want me to fuck you from behind?*

"*Put that ass up in the air.*

"*Shove that ass up so I can fuck it.*"

"*Oh baby, shove it in me!*

"*God, nothing feels like you do.*

"*No one does what you do to me.*

"*Your balls are hitting my clit – you're gonna make me come just like that.*"

"*I love making you come.*"

"*Everything you do is perfect, every angle you hit is exactly where you should be!*

"*You make it feel good...*

"*It just feels like it can't get any deeper.*

"*It almost feels like it's too deep inside me.*"

"*Stick that ass up in the air, you little alley cat you.*

"*Whose pussy is that?*

"*Tell me whose pussy that is. – Say it's Clint's pussy.*"

"*Only yours.*

"*Only you, only you!*"

"*Stick that ass up!*

"*That's my ass! My pussy!*"

"*I want to feel you cum all over me!*"

"*Stick that pussy up! That's my pussy, stick it up!*

"*Whose pussy is it?*"

"*Take me! Take me! Take me!*"

"*Spread those legs.*

"*Let me shove it in you!*

"*What do you want?*"

"*I just want you. I want you deep inside me. No one's ever been there before – I swear to you – I can't even believe what you do to me – everything you do makes me wet!*"

"*You are soaking fucking wet!*"

"*Oh baby, fuck me!*"

"*Whose ass?*"

"It's yours.

"God, I'm gonna cum all over your big hard cock – your fucking cock!"

"Stick that up in the air!"

"I'm cumming! I'm cumming! I'm cumming! Now! Now! Now!"

"Who makes that pussy cum?"

"Only you!

"I want you to cum all over me! Please cum all over me! Please!"

"I want to feel you squirt all over me!"

"You want to feel my hot cum?"

"Please!

"So much cum all over me – I love that!"

"How many times did you cum tonight?"

"I don't know – I can't count."

"Did you cum when I went down on you?

"Did you cum when I fucked you?

"You are the hottest lover I have ever had. The way you open to me – you make me feel so welcome inside you."

"When you're not inside me, I just feel empty."

"I just want to be inside you all the time.

"Why don't you suck on me. Get down on your hands and knees and suck on me like a good little animal servant.

"Get right between my legs and suck me.

"That's the cock that makes you feel good.

"That's the cock that makes you cum.

"Suck that cock.

"You like sucking that cock?"

"I just can't leave it alone. Whenever it's hard, I just want to suck on it. And when it's soft, I want to make it hard. And when you have clothes on I want to take them off, and when you don't I can't resist it."

"That's it, suck it hard.

"Okay, now take it all the way deep in your throat and just hold it in there. Suck it hard. Open up and suck it in there.

"Yeah – in your throat, yeah!

"Now turn around and back that pussy up to my dick! Back it in here!"

"I want to feel you cum all over me!

"Oh baby, it's so deep!"

"Your pussy is so fucking wet!

"Your pussy is so fucking wide open now!

"All of a sudden it's opening up.

"I'm so fucking sweaty. You make me so hot and sweaty.

"You make me feel like a tiger!

"My pussy!

"It has my name on it!

"I feel your tits sticking onto the side of my body.

"I just want to fill you full of cum.

"I just want to pump out all the cum inside you."

"I don't know what you do to me. What are you doing to me?"

"I'm fucking you.

"I love your pussy. I love your tits. I love your ass. I love your throat."

"Grab my tits!

"Everything that you do just makes my fingers and toes curl up!

"It just makes me get shivers up and down my spine, the way you pump up inside of me."

"Kiss me!

"You are my woman! I knew you were mine the first time I met you.

"The first time I kissed you – I knew you were my woman."

"No one else – I don't want anyone else – I just want you inside me – what you do to me, oh what you do to me!

"God, you just climb on top of me – every way you change, it's like we just tangle our legs together and you just shove your cock inside of me – everything you do, every different angle feels so amazing."

"Oooh yeah!

"You want to feel me cum?

"Put that pussy up in the air!"

"Fuck me, take me, okay take me, fuck me, oh baby do me!"

"Let me grab those tits of yours – oh yeah!"

"Oh fuck me baby fuck me!"

"It goes in so easy!

"Put that pussy up in the air!

"I want to split you open and fuck you!

"Oh baby, oh God!"

"I feel my legs wrapped around your back holding you against me, holding you deep inside me!

"I feel everything you do to me!

"Your balls are just hitting my clit!"

"If you cum, I'll cum."

"I want to feel you between my tits."

"You want me to fuck your tits?

"Suck me baby!

"Slobber all over it!

"Fucking suck it, baby!

"Oh, I know you care about me when you put it in your throat like that.

"Let me fuck your tits, baby. I want to cum all over your tits."

"Let me suck on your cock when you fuck my tits!

"Baby, squirt it all over me!

"I want it to explode all over me, all over my face!"

"I like it when you squeeze your tits around my cock!"

"Oh baby, fuck it so hard!

"I want to feel you cum all over my face!

"Pump it all over me, baby! Everywhere, all over me!

"Oh baby, fuck it!

"Oh baby, pump it all over my neck!

"Oh baby, do me!

"Yeah yeah yeah!

"I love it when it squirts all over me!"

"Let me fuck that pussy again!

"It's really sloppy wet!"

"We're all sweaty and sloppy and sticky and wet!

"All sweaty wet and sloppy -- God you feel great!"

"Tell me what you want. What do you want? Tell me what you want – tell me what you want..."

"I want to turn on the lights and see you – is that okay? I gotta see you.

"Look at you – look at you!"

"God, you get so deep inside me!

"Cum all over me! Will you please?

"I'm gonna cum again.

"I get chills all through my body, all the way from my head all the way down to my feet!

"You're gonna make me squirt – the way you're hitting me, you're gonna make me squirt!"

"I like when your legs are around my neck.

"I want to feel you squirt.

"I can feel the sweat dripping down my spine, all the way down my ass.

"I can still hear the music from the show tonight!

"I can still feel us dancing to that salsa music."

"Your big hard cock just ramming into me – just like this...

"Spread me open and fuck me – oh deep inside me!

"This is just what I was dreaming of – just what I needed.

"Oh God, you feel amazing – God you feel so good – oh God what you do to me."

"Come on top of me and suck me for a while – okay?

"Look at your big beautiful tits hanging down over me.

"Are you my little cum-slurper?

"My little sweetheart sweetie cutie-pie – you turn me on like no other woman."

"I love to take you into my throat... I love how it feels when its not really hard, I can slip it into my throat when it's not yet hard, and how it gets harder in my throat and I can keep going."

"I love how you suck me, how you take me all the way in, all the way down to the base.

"Feel me getting harder in your mouth?

"Are you gonna make me cum like that?

"You gonna suck the cum out of me?

"Would you like to suck the cum out of my cock?"

"Ohhhhhhhhhhhhhhhhhhhhhhhh-ohhhhhhhhhhhhhhhhh!"

"You're so fucking drooling. All sloppy drooling – I love it.

"If you want to make me cum, use your hand too. Fuckin' suck it and squeeze it.

"Suck it and squeeze it, yeah!

"I want to get on my knees and have you on your hands and knees. I know you can make me cum like that.

"Seeing you like that – oh yeah – seeing this beautiful heart-shaped ass in front of my eyes...

"Yeah, lean down on it!

"Are you my little cum-slave? My little cum-slurping slave?

"Oh my God, you're incredible!

"There's so much cum all over the sheets! Cum and blood and blowjob slime!

"I love having you as my lover..."

"I love making love with you."

"You are such an incredible, phenomenal, fantastic, wonderful, amazing lover... And such a hot slut – especially for a Jewish girl!"

"There's just cum everywhere!"

GODDESS WORSHIP

I had been very curious about the Goddess Worship ceremony that I'd read about on GoddessTemple.com.

Goddess Natalia said, "I never do that with my clients. It's much too intimate. Corynna keeps trying to convince me to do it, but I'm not going to put myself in that position with just anyone."

I scheduled a lunch date with Dr. Clarke, and went over to her house at the appointed time. She was in a great mood when I got there, and when I asked why she was so happy she showed me a large diamond engagement ring on her hand, and told me that she had become engaged to Charles Muir.

"But I thought he was married to Caroline Muir?" I wondered aloud.

"He is," she confirmed.

"Well, then I guess I'm very happy for you all."

"Thank you, Clint."

After Goddess Natalia told me about her experience at the Muirs' seminar, I went home and checked them out on the Internet. From what I could gather, they lived in Maui and spent a lot of time traveling the world, partying and having sex with lots of people, and teaching people how to have great sex. Goddess Mare listed them as major teachers of hers, Natalia and Anthea had "studied" with Charles. The guy seemed like he had the ultimate life. And he quickly became someone I looked up to. When I heard that he was married and yet also engaged to Dr. Clarke, the head Goddess of Los Angeles, he instantly became my idol.

I asked, "How's your live-in boyfriend Evan dealing with your engagement to Charles?"

She said, "Not too well, but that's understandable."

What an understatement. I said, "Corynna, with all the Goddesses you know, and with all the different ceremonies that they do, you should do a video series with me illustrating each of the different rituals. For example, it would be great to do a video about Goddess Worship. I could be in it, you could direct it, and we'll get a Goddess from Goddess Temple to perform the ceremony with me."

She liked the idea, and agreed to direct the project and to get us a Goddess to be in the video.

There was a scaldingly sexy new Goddess who worked using the name Lilith, and Corynna arranged for her to come down from San Francisco for the weekend production.

The goal was to document a real Goddess Worship ritual so that people could learn what it would be like if they had such a session with one of the Goddesses on GoddessTemple.com or if they wanted to create the scenario privately with their lover.

It was a great learning experience, and it turned out to be a film I am truly proud of.

I arrived at the location for the shoot in Topanga Canyon early in the morning to find Dr. Clarke and her mother busy arranging flowers and preparing the set. Corynna introduced me to the Goddess Lilith, and to the cameraman, Tor, who she had gotten to work in exchange for her promise to give him a mega-blowjob. About thirty minutes after I arrived, we began the ritual.

> *A wise man took me to the top of a canyon...*
> *He said close both eyes so you can see with your*
> *other eye.*
> -Jillian Speer

THE RITUAL

When a woman is fully honored, her love automatically spills over to her man, her family, and ultimately to the world. Goddess Worship is an ancient ritual seeded in ancient tradition. Combined with modern sensual healing, it becomes an erotic journey into a woman's sensual self and her Goddess nature.

OFFERING

<u>The man should always bring a Goddess an offering of cut flowers.</u> A living/potted plant is not a good substitute, as the flowers must actually be sacrificed to the Goddess in her honor. They also serve as a reminder of the preciousness of life, and the importance of living fully in the moment, while we can. Do not underestimate Flower Power.

"I invite you to be as Yin, and as slow, and as delicate as you can be. And see me as an opening flower. Remember to give without expectations or an agenda. And always ask if you are unsure or need guidance."

FOOD

At the beginning, the Goddess and her devotee should feed each other fruits, such as grapes, mango, melon, or "living foods" such as clams or oysters on the half-shell…

Lovers may also share DRINKS of wine, juices, or waters, as the beginning of this ritual is intended to acclimate the two people to being in each other's presence…

And to begin building a shared bond that comes with sharing food.

Tantric rituals came into existence because of the prevailing practice of arranged marriages in ancient India.

Often a girl of sixteen would be married off to a man thirty or forty years her senior…

These people shared no love – they hardly knew each other. And yet <u>intimacy had to be created between the couple.</u>

The Tantric rituals were a formalized approach to creating such intimacy between married "strangers"…

Walking the couple through familiarization processes intended to create TRUST…

RELAXATION…

And DESIRE.

BALANCE

Goddess Lilith and I balanced our energies...

Sitting cross-legged and close to each other...

With left palm up and right palm down...

Cupping each other's hands...

We created a CIRCUIT of ENERGY...

Looking into each other's eyes...

Breathing deeply...

Allowing our HEART RATES to synchronize...

Gaining TRUST...

RELAXING with each other...

Creating two circuits of energy – one with our hands, and one with our breath.

Through your right hand, you give...

Through your left hand, you receive...

"Into my left I receive through my heart, and out my right I give to you...

"You receive and through your heart you give to me again.

"On the in-breath, breathing up from your root, up through your spine and through the crown of your head...

"Receiving loving energy...

"And as you exhale, send it out and give it back to your partner.

"Visualizing light circulating through our arms and to our hearts...

"Sharing loving, sensual energy...

"We come together through touch...

"Uniting our senses and our breath...

"Harmonizing..."

At the conclusion of this section of the ceremony, we bring our hands together, look into each other's eyes, and exchange the Tantric lovers' pledge...

"The highest in me honors the highest in you... Namaste."

OFFERING TOUCH

The breath is a conduit of energy through your body.

The best way to address a woman with your touch is with a touch that gives, and not a touch that takes. This way you can send your loving energy through your eyes, through your hands, through your lingam, and always remember to use a touch that gives and not a touch that takes.

Remind yourself of the love you are sending with each touch and with each stroke…

GODDESS WORSHIP MASSAGE

Have the Goddess lie down, and begin with her feet.

Remember to spend enough time on each part of the body so that she may feel relaxed and at ease with the worshipper's touch.

Goddesses love having their feet kissed.

When you're ready, you can move up her legs one at a time…

Tantalizing just around her yoni, but not quite touching…

Remember to ask if the pressure is okay, if she desires more…

Long strokes moving up the body…

Visualizing the strokes moving energy up toward her heart…

This is the worshipper's offering…

Remembering the inside of her thighs is a very tender, sensitive area…

She may enjoy it if you go deeper and kneed her thighs…

Move slowly and sensually – this will relax her even more…

Remember that you can send loving energy through your touch to any part of her body…

Kissing and licking her knees and up her thighs…

Up the midsection of her torso…

But <u>don't get too carried away in your own arousal –
remember the Goddess is the one being worshipped...</u>

MAKING SMALL FINGERTIP CIRCLES AROUND
HER AREOLAS...

<u>Breathing hot breaths on her nipples...</u>

VERY LIGHTLY TEASING WITH YOUR LIPS...

Just enough for her to be asking for more...

Asking for you to kiss her nipples...

Be aware that sometimes a Goddess's breasts are tender...

Sometimes they're extremely sensitive to your touch...

Don't forget, there's a whole body there...

<u>The back of her rib cage...</u>

Her shoulders...

Upper arms...

Fingers...

Wrists...

TONING

Toning is the tantric practice of making noises with your
mouth – humming, moaning, or making any kind of vibrational
noise.   THIS HAS SUCH TREMENDOUS POWER, you
cannot even imagine what the impact will be until you try it.

The devotee may chant sounds or the words "Om shanti
shanti..."

While looking into the Goddess's eyes...

Or even directly into erogenous zones of her body...

Such as above her yoni...

Bringing your lips to contact her pubic hair...

Focusing only on the vibrations moving through your chest
and out your mouth...

<u>Bringing your hand to her heart...</u>

Then <u>massaging energy up the centerline of her body...</u>

Up from her yoni, up through her heart, up through the
centerline of her body...

It's good to repeat most strokes at least three times.

Paying attention to her womanly hips...

Then turning her over to lie on her stomach...

Massaging up her feet and the backs of her legs...

Paying lots of yummy attention to her bottom...

<u>Kissing and licking the backs of her thighs...</u>

She may enjoy the way your whiskers or beard tickles her...

You can take your thumbs and ride them up either side of her spine, several times...

And when you get to the top, you can grab her shoulders and massage them...

Using the pads of your thumb, you can vary the degrees of pressure...

Then, standing at her head, you can massage down her spine with one hand on either side of her spine...

YAB YUM

Be seated with the man cross-legged and the Goddess in his lap with her legs wrapped around his waist (this is known as *yab yum*)...

And breathe the breath of the Goddess...

As you inhale, she exhales...

As she exhales, you inhale...

Mouths close...

Hearts aligned...

"As we reciprocate our breath, our bodies become aligned with each other's energy."

Lightly massage or rub each other's backs...

YONI SATTVA

Begin by slowly massaging the inside of her thighs, close to her yoni...

Riding up, touching her pubic bone with some pressure...

Just doing that with your own touch...
Preparing her yoni to be touched...
To be caressed...
Think of using a therapeutic touch...
Often times women are touched either clinically or purely sexually...

It's nice to be paid attention to in a different way...

All the way up the skin beside her lips to her pubic bone...

Spread her lips to open her labia like an unfolding flower...

With your index or middle finger, do light strokes between her inner and outer labia...

Make circles all the way around, from the top to the bottom...

GO VERY SLOWLY AND VERY CONSCIOUSLY

Stopping at the bottom for just a second...

Riding up and maybe just being conscious of her clitoris at the top...

Holding your finger at the very bottom for a long moment...

As if you were going to enter, but not entering.

With one hand you can pull back the hood of her clitoris, and with a very light, fingertip touch, circulate around her clitoris but not quite on it...

Breathing lightly on her clitoris...

And with one hand on her heart...

Looking into her eyes...

Ask her, "Goddess, may I please kiss your yoni?"

If she permits, with very softly, ever so lightly, lay your tongue on her clitoris and just hold it there...

Very softly...

Making a similar move with your tongue as you were with your fingers – around – all the way around...

Sending her love through your mouth...

SENDING HER ALL OF YOUR WONDERFUL MASCULINE ENERGY…

Softly pulling away sometimes…

Teasing her…

You can bite the outer labia if you like…

Nice tender kisses…

Up and down, down the center of her yoni…

Nibbles and licks…

Softly, softly, softly…

And paying attention to the rest of her with your hands…

All of her body…

"MAY I ENTER YOUR TEMPLE?"

If she allows, using your middle finger, very, very slowly reach in, <u>using a motion as if you were calling her to come closer to you…</u>

Deeply feeling the difference in tissue inside her yoni…

It's smooth on the walls…

And right there in the middle, it's rough and ridgelike…

That's her sacred spot…

Move in closer to that spot and <u>check in with her to make sure that your pressure is okay…</u>

She'll tell you if you should press deeper…

Stay right there, right on that…

Pressing on her sacred spot…

RECEIVE HER FEMININE ENERGY THROUGH YOUR FINGER INTO YOUR BODY

<u>Let it heal you…</u>

<u>Let it nurture you…</u>

VARY YOUR TOUCH…

You can do circles…

You can do taps…

The texture may change…

Or the spot may move down a bit…

Keep searching…

Keep calling her to come closer to you…

And you can lick her a little bit as you call her to you…

You may ask if she wants more pressure now…

And if she does, give it to her…

Licking a second finger and inserting it inside her yoni…

Moving your fingers in and out faster…

With more pressure…

She may pull your hair or squeeze your hand on her heart as she climaxes…

And when she does, slow it down a bit…

Lightly, lightly, lightly…

Come outside a bit and play with the outside…

Touch her clit…

Rub her yoni between your fingers…

And just love her for the gifts she's given…

Be gentle with her…

Gentle, gentle…

Slow down with the movement and get very focused…

Very concentrated on where you're at…

On the sacredness of where you're touching…

Come up close to look into her eyes…

Bringing all of your awareness to the tip of your finger…

SENDING HER ALL OF YOUR ENERGY…

To bring her to another climax with your intention and your love…

"Love, love, love, beautiful Goddess… Love, love, love…"

Being with her…

Being there for her…

As she deals with whatever emotions come up for her…

Be they in the form of tears or laughter…

Just gentle yin touches…

Slowing down your touch…

BEFORE YOU EXIT, LET HER KNOW

Tell her that you'll be leaving her body...

You may never want to exit!

It's so wonderful!

Tell her: "I'm going to exit now."

She may respond, "Thank you, thank you, for your imprints of love."

Now just hold her yoni, cupping it with the palm of your hand, so she can feel your warmth and know that you haven't gone anywhere...

You've left your beautiful energy inside of her...

"Thank you, Goddess!"

"Thank you, Divine Consort!"

INTEGRATION

Spoon and cuddle with her...

Integrate the energy you just shared...

Rubbing each other's arms...

Kissing her neck from your position behind her body...

Keeping one hand over her heart to maintain the flow of energy.

GRATITUDE

Living with gratitude enriches every aspect of life, including Goddess Worship rituals, meals, work, family – everything. It's especially true with sex.

Next time you're intimate with someone, take a moment to be thankful for the experience of being with that person, of being able to physically experience the joys of intimacy, for not being alone.

At the conclusion of Goddess Worship or any ritual experience, you might share the following words with your partner.

The Goddess may say:

"I'd like to thank you for sharing yourself with me…

"For honoring me in this way.

"Take this experience into your life…

"Share it with your family, with your friends, with your lovers…

"Let this energy continue to be a part of you…

"And let's also give thanks to the universe, for giving us such a blessing to be here today…

"And we can just send it out to the planet for her nurturing and her healing."

The Worshipper may say:

"Thank you, Goddess, for sharing the great feminine powers with me, for letting me experience the flow of Great Goddess Energy, and for giving me this opportunity to worship your divinity."

THE MOST POWERFUL EJACULATION

Foolishly, I did not schedule a "God Worship" video shoot the same day as the "Goddess Worship" shoot, and ended up in an extremely energized state when we wrapped.

I invited Goddess Lilith to lunch at Gladstone's 4 Fish afterward, and learned about her life as a Goddess in San Francisco and about the boyfriend with whom she lived. "I'm practically engaged!" she confessed with internal consternation. She was a very sexual person, and I could tell that she loved being "freaky" like she had been earlier in the day with me, but at the same time she felt guilty and would only let herself go so far.

Nonetheless, I was most determined, and I resolved to stay with her if possible until I was able to release the pent-up and frustrated energy that had been created within me during my devotional worship of the Goddess.

She said, "I don't know if you'd be interested, but later I'm going to a party with a bunch of Goddesses at Goddess Anthea's house."

I said, "I've already had the honor of attending an ejaculation ceremony at Anthea's Love Temple."

She said, "Then great, you can come."

I thought, *I certainly HOPE so!*

That night Goddess Lilith, Goddess Anthea, another San Francisco Goddess named Melia, her boyfriend Tom, and I all took Ecstasy, smoked some pot, and got naked on the futon in the living room of Anthea's new Love Temple in West Hollywood.

Right after we all took the Ecstasy, Goddess Lilith announced, "Clint, you had the honor of doing my sacred spot earlier today, so tonight Tom will have the honor."

Tom was psyched! And they went right at it on the futon.

That left me with Melia and Anthea, neither of whom were anywhere near as attractive as the ravishing Goddess Lilith. And neither of whom were into me.

Anthea, I had learned, was primarily into lesbian encounters. And Melia seemed most captivated by her.

So while Melia knelt between Anthea's legs, I massaged her shoulders and got stuck in my head tripping on the Ecstasy.

My head was actually between Anthea's head and Lilith's, and after a while I started synchronizing my mental energy with theirs...

And pretty soon things started getting very intense...

All of a sudden I heard Melia shout, "Yeah! Come on sister, show me what you've got!"

Then Anthea arched her back and raised her hips up off the ground, and in a moment I heard a HUGE WOOOSHING sound...

I looked up to see what was going on, and I was astonished by what I saw.

An inch-thick jet stream of amrita blasted out from between Anthea's legs.

Melia was ecstatic!

The amrita splashed up off Melia's chest to ricochet further up into the air and spray the entire futon with the force of a sprinkler on the side of a freeway.

I had to shield my eyes with my forearm to keep from getting blinded by the spray!

This continued for what seemed like twenty seconds...

Spraying and splashing up into the air!

It was unbelievable.

The most forceful squirt of female ejaculate I've ever seen in my life!

EJACULATORY DIFFERENCES

Some women "squirt," while others "gush." Some women ejaculate a few teaspoons of liquid, while others, like Anthea, soak endless loads of towels during the course of a night.

Some women squirt a few inches or feet, while others send out virtual geysers of amrita. Sometimes the nature of the amrita or the ejaculation itself varies from occasion to occasion even with the same woman.

All of this is irrelevant. It's not the amount, force, flavor, or frequency of ejaculations that matter. What matters is a woman's ability and willingness to let go and tap into the awesome powers of her Goddess spot and the amrita which flows from the fountainhead of sexual power for women and the men who love them.

New Sex Advisor #75 © 2001 Clint Arthur & www.NewSex.org
Her Words Made Me Cum

It was one of our classic weekend days by the pool...

Feasting on raw oysters and tuna tartare with natural sparkling water in the shade of her orange tree...

Then she got in the shallow end and floated on a raft until I took the first few steps into the cool water...

She paddled over to where her mouth suctioned in my stiffening erection, deep, deep, deep...

I hadn't expected to get so turned on, but Cheryl's become quite the little oral expert, and before I knew it I got caught up in my exhilaration and started really fucking her head...

Holding it in my hands and skulling her hard...

To where I shot a huge load deep inside her throat...

She just held me down deep and sucked with so much affection – I could really feel the love...

And the lust.

A short while later I had her lie down on the raft again and went down on her tasty temple of love...

Toning and vibrating her clitoris with my mouth and tongue and hot breaths with sounds...

Increasing the pitch and intensity as her energy level built...

She came from that after about ten minutes of heavenly delight...

Then I took her off the raft and held her in my arms in chest-high water as I expertly strummed and pulsed chords of love on her G-spot...

"I'm shooting!" she moaned almost immediately.

Then she really started to cum and stopped talking and just started moaning that high-pitched alley-cat-in-heat sound...

And after she came a few times like that, I spun her body in the water and pumped inside her with my renewed erection.

Her ejaculations always get me hard...

We fucked and grabbed each other frantically for a long time, and she ejaculated underwater several times...

Then I started reaching around and fingering her ass with one finger, then with two fingers – and all of a sudden I realized I need to be fucking her ass on a regular basis...

"Let's go inside and oil you up," I whispered.

She was hesitant, but acquiesced...

So we had some anal sex for a while at the foot of her bed, and while it's good I'm still not an anal maniac, so we returned to the pool for more "regular sex" in the shallows...

And although I really didn't want to cum again – so as to preserve my kundalini energy – I got turned on by the idea of jacking my load into her open mouth and all over her face...

So I told her, "When I cum, I want you to open your mouth and I'll shoot all over your face," and she said, "Okay, baby, whatever you want..."

I went in and got the oil and oiled up for a smooth masturbatory rub, but while it was sexy and fun to do, I wasn't making any orgasmic progress at all until she started talking dirty to me...

"Oh baby, I want to feel your hot cum shoot all over my face..."

As she's rubbing her tits and cupping my balls...

"Shoot your big hot cock all over me..."

And words to that effect...

And amazingly, before I could even realize it was happening, I was very much back into a cumming mode...

Shooting stripes of hot jizz right up the middle of her face...

All over her throat and nose...

It was a true porn-movie moment...

Such a huge load...

And all because of her words.

If you want to hear Cheryl in prime form, check out our audio CD *Master Sex Talk,* available only at www.NewSex.org

Use your mouth to engage your lover's ears and mind...

You'll be glad you did.

Sincerely, Your New Sex Advisor.

<u>REVIEW QUIZ</u>

1. What a man should say during sex: _____!

2. The most powerful erogenous zone in the body is located between our _____.

3. Talking during sex activates your _____ and your _____.

4. A man should always bring a Goddess an offering of _____ _____.

5. To promote intimacy, a couple should _____ their energies.

6. The highest in me honors the highest in you... _____.

7. In the art of sexual toning, stimulation occurs with sound and _____.

8. Living with _____ enriches every aspect of life.

9. Integrate sexual energy after lovemaking by _____ and _____.

6
ORAL SEX
MASTERY

GENERAL GUIDELINES

For some people, oral sex is more intimate
than sexual intercourse.

When going down on someone, pick a position that's
comfortable for both giver and receiver.

You can receive oral sex while standing, sitting,
or lying flat on your back, or while on your knees.

Prior to going down on a woman, just breathe hot breaths on
her vagina for a long time.
This will drive her CRAZY!

Feel free to include foods in your oral lovemaking, such as
honey, whipped cream, chocolate sauce, and fruits such as
grapes, melon, bananas and sweet berries. Red wine stings!

Gently sucking a woman's clitoris (as if it were a tiny penis)
gets it sensitive and tender in preparation for licking and
pressing movements intended to bring climax.

Sucking a clitoris too hard or too long can make it
too sensitive or too swollen.

Turn yourself on while giving oral sex by watching your
lover's reactions and by observing his or her sex parts as they
change and react to your touches.

It's easy to become an "Expert" at oral sex if you ask
questions, observe, care about the person,
and get into the experience.

Many women who don't like oral sex
feel that way because they've never had it
from someone who did it well.
Or they've never done it well.

A woman should tell
her man when something feels good –
and to keep doing it.

Men often don't have the patience to bring a woman to
climax with oral sex, and because of that,
some women don't know how great sex can be.

What a woman wants from oral sex:
tenderness
and
attention.

Going down on a woman gets her attention on sex,
gets her ready for sexual intercourse,
warmed up and aroused.

"When I wake up in the morning with my lover going down on
me, the static of daily tasks hasn't started yet,
so my mind is really clear, free, and open to just DO instead of
THINK – so in just minutes you can be at a complete peak
level."

GREAT oral sex is often wet and sloppy.

"Oral sex in the morning is like a really good dream
that feels very real."

Use oral sex to prolong a sexual encounter.
30 minutes of oral sex
+ 5 minutes of sexual intercourse
= 35 minutes of sex.

The most important aspect of great oral sex is DESIRE.

The experience of oral sex in a public place can be
thrilling. The "naughty" danger of being so exposed
could really turn you or your lover on.
Try an alley, stairway, elevator, bathroom,
train, plane, park, or parking garage.

Sometimes it's fun to fantasize during oral sex.
Pretend you're giving to or receiving from a celebrity,
high-school sweetheart, someone you have a crush on.
Other times it's best to be fully present in the moment.
Use "movie-star techniques" to be more present during
oral sex: look, listen, touch, smell, and taste what's going
on to be most present during oral sex.
Enjoy the saltiness, the sounds of your lover's moans,
his heavy breathing, your own licking,
the musky aroma, feel his hardness in your mouth,
or watch the sensual shape of his body
as he pleasures you.

We're accustomed to playing sexual baseball:
going from first, to second, third,
and finally scoring a home run.
But sometimes going from home plate back to third
base, and back and forth, can be amazing.

You might enjoy videotaping your oral sex to show or
see what works best, or to critique style and technique.

Watching a video of someone going down on you
while that person (or someone else) goes down on you can be a
real erotic thrill.

Every man's desire: his penis sucked by
a capable woman who wants to do it and enjoys it.

Give your lover great visual and aural stimulation while going
down on him. The sights and sounds of you enjoying servicing
him can be the greatest thrill.

How much oral sex is enough or too much is a matter of
personal preference. Most men would be
very happy to get it once a week on a regular basis.

Remember that toning is the tantric practice of making noises
with your mouth while performing oral sex on your lover.
Hum, moan, or make any kind of vibrational noise to
add a powerful new element to oral lovemaking.

Natural and other flavors can alter your whole mindset about
oral sex. "Wet" brand flavors such as Piña Colada, Vanilla, and
Berry can add sweetness and "spice" to lovemaking.

Bathing together or giving your lover a bath can offer a sexy
start to oral lovemaking. A bath and/or douche
will remove many unpleasant odors.

It's awesome to watch your lover on her knees servicing you in
the shower while warm water runs down your body.

Oral sex during a long drive helps pass the time
and makes both lovers feel special about the trip.
Who cares if truck drivers see?
Pull over and park if it gets too wild!

69 allows both partners to give and receive.
It is VERY intimate.

Three positions for 69
• Woman on top
• Man on top
• Man and woman on their sides

Take it all in as deep as you can, suck hard,
and just hold that as long as you can.

Suck it in and out, up and down, with a steady rhythm,
for a long time. Slowly build the rhythm, speed, and
pressure of your sucking.
Keep going until your mouth is vibrating
on your lover's sex, then go back to slow, soft motion
and build it up again.

Many women enjoy sucking a flaccid penis as much or
even more than an erect one.

"You can wake me up with a blowjob
any day, any time."

WHAT WOMEN ENJOY ABOUT GOING DOWN ON A MAN:

- "Feeling the power"
- The control
- The taste of his juices
- Feeling the smoothness of his skin
- Making him harder
- The intimacy
- Giving him pleasure
- Serving him
- Doing it well
- Just doing it
- His gratitude
- "Tasting the sweetness"

POSITIONS FOR HER TO GO DOWN ON HIM:

On her knees
69
On her hands and knees
Lying on her back with her head hanging over the side of the bed.
Kneeling or sitting beside him.*

*Kneeling or sitting beside the man is
the least effective way to go down on him.
The angle is wrong for his penis and for her neck.
It's uncomfortable for him and her.

New Sex Advisor #58 © 2001 Clint Arthur & www.NewSex.org
Woman Disappears During New Sex™

I love watching Cheryl on her hands and knees blowing me.

Her beautiful shape in front of me, serving me with her mouth going all the way up and down the length of my shaft...

Her hands cupped under my balls, subtly squeezing...

She's even progressed to the point where she can get me in her throat like that...

And the depth is intense.

Especially because fellatio is such a great tool for turning her on.

Luckily her oral attitude has always been very positive. In my seminars I talk about how useful it is for the woman to suck the man's penis – it's impossible for her to deny the reality of a sexual experience when she's got a dick in her mouth...

And such a great part of the power of New Sex™ is that it breaks down a woman's natural denial of her own sexual desire...

It takes a woman to the point where she WANTS it.

So after sucking me for a good long time that Sunday afternoon on the boat, I knew she'd be wet...

And she was...

Soaking...

We dogged for a long time, which we both love, but then I stopped and pulled out and laid her down on her back...

"I don't want to come," I said to her with heavy breaths... "But I want you to come." Then I dove between her legs and put my mouth into high gear.

That's another very subtle sexual technique for you: Don't be afraid to go "backward" around the "bases." Just because you've "gone all the way" doesn't mean you can't or shouldn't go back to "third base"...

Or even "second" or "first" – a woman will never get tired of kissing, or petting, or whatever kind of non-intercourse attention you give her.

As I'm going down on her, I gently insert my fingers…

I begin to strum her G-spot strings…

Music sings out of her mouth like a concert…

A chorus of moans and wails of sexual activation.

I know just how to vary my touch…

And exactly what to expect as her body shows me specific, precisely predictable signposts along the route to female ejaculation…

And as the amrita fluids gush from deep inside her…

My arousal grows…

To a point where I can no longer control myself…

I must fuck her…

She's moaning "I'm coming! I'm coming!"

I pump and thrust and squeeze and crush her body in my powerful embrace…

"Oh, I'm coming!" she wails as her body shudders… "Shoot it on me!"

And though I'd wanted to preserve my precious, powerful kundalini energy, I feel myself in the grips of forces bigger than myself…

And I pull out to jack a hot splatter all over her heaving, sexy stomach and massive double-Ds…While she humps her torso under my balls and makes sexy noises and whimpers.

Collapsing onto her chest with deep exhalations…

After a while she pants into my ear: "I disappeared there for a while. I was just cumming and cumming and cumming – I didn't know where I was."

In this story are several secrets for mastering female sexual pleasure and taking yourself to new heights of personal pleasure along with your lover.

Don't you deserve to take the next step on your own sexual revolution? Get your own copy of *New Sex Now* – the only instructional video GUARANTEED to teach you exactly how to enjoy simultaneous EJACULATIONS with any woman.

There is a vast and astounding world of new sexual frontiers waiting for you to explore with some lucky person.

The knowledge and skills you will acquire with the New Sex™ techniques will provide you with tremendous self-confidence and assurance pervading every aspect of your life.

MAKE YOUR MAN FEEL LIKE
$1,000,000.00

In the middle of the day go down on him,
swallow,
clean him off with a warm, wet washcloth,
thank him –
and enjoy it!
Do that during his
lunch break at work
and see how soon
he gets promoted!

ORAL SEX TECHNIQUES TO GIVE HIM PLEASURE

Lick his scrotum, anus, shaft, head of his penis, and any
other part of his body that is erotic for him.*

Run your lips over his scrotum, anus, shaft, head and
erotically charged body parts.*

Suck on his testicles, anus, shaft, head of his penis,
and other erotic body parts.*

Stroke his shaft, up and down with a tight grip while
sucking with your mouth.
Let your saliva lubricate your hand movements.

*Every part of a man's body is potentially an erotic hot
spot you can make love to with your mouth.

Be aware: some "teeth" can be fun,
but too much hurts!

ORAL SEX TECHNIQUES TO GIVE HER PLEASURE

Lick her nipples, breasts, thighs, labia, clitoris, pubic hair region, G-spot, and all inside her vagina and other erotic areas*

Swish, swirl, and/or vibrate your tongue on her nipples, breasts, lips, clitoris, G-spot and other erotic areas.*

Nibble her sex parts with your teeth,
and/or bite them only as hard as is pleasurable to her.

Tickle her clit with your beard or scruff.

Run your lips over the parts of her body that turn her on.*

*Every part of a woman's body is potentially an erotic hot spot which you can make love to with your mouth.

POSITIONS FOR HIM TO GO DOWN ON HER
- On his stomach while she lies flat on her back.
- 69
- Sitting or kneeling beside her.
- On his knees while she stands or sits.
- From behind while she's on all fours or sticking it up in the air.
- Hanging his head down (upside down) while she lies flat on her stomach or kneels.

Tongue her G-spot while she fingers her clit.

DEEP THROAT

"I've instructed many women on how to deep throat;
those that could do it loved me;
those who couldn't, didn't."

The most important factor in being able to deep throat:
love.
The 2nd key factor in being able to deep throat:
desire.

Great deep throat is always sloppy and slimy.
(Have a towel handy if that bothers you.)

When a woman learns how to deep throat, it is vital that
she stays in control.

"Gag Reflex" during deep throat will eventually be
mastered if the woman stays in control.

DEEP THROAT BENEFITS FOR WOMEN

"It's like a different penis. It seems to get absolutely
harder and bigger, to the point where it's stretching the skin
to its absolute maximum – which means MORE PENIS!"

"Deep throat seems to make the penis more sensitive.
And it makes him crazy. And crazy in sex usually translates
to GREAT SEX."

"Deep throat 69 gets us both to a more erotic point
quickly. That's great in the morning. Deep throat 69 gets
you the equivalent of an hour into sex in just four or five
minutes, so you're both to an amazingly erotic point where
you're relaxed and ready to cum."

In deep throat, desire will triumph over size, especially when powered by love.

"The smallest woman I ever had sex with had no problem deep throating me."

Sometimes it feels great to use your mouth and hands; other times a mouth alone feels best.

HOW TO LEARN DEEP THROAT

The key is that the WOMAN MUST STAY IN CONTROL.

The man lies on his back.

She gets on top of him...

And, <u>GOING AS SLOWLY AS SHE WANTS</u>, TAKES AS MUCH OF HIS PENIS IN HER MOUTH AS SHE CAN...

To the point where she STARTS TO FEEL LIKE SHE'S GOING TO GAG...

Then just hold it there as long as possible.

The man must not push her head down...

He must not buck up or thrust up his hips...

He just lies there and lets her experiment and get used to having his penis going farther and farther into her throat.

It's like a puzzle. Each man's penis will fit into each woman's throat a different way, based on the shape of his penis, the angle she's holding her throat, and so on.

The best way for her to determine what works best is as she's pushing the penis into her throat she should change the angle of her throat and of her body slightly, moving her head and neck in a combination of angles to find what lines them up perfectly. It may mean getting up on her knees to be higher up over the penis, or lowering herself down a bit, but eventually she will find the right angle.

The best way to find the right angle for you is to begin deep throating while the penis is not fully erect. If she can find the right angle when the penis is not fully erect; that will be the same angle when it is fully erect.

THIS MAY BE UNCOMFORTABLE FOR HER

She'll have to overcome her natural gag reflex.

It will be a very tight fit...

Eventually, if you do it right, the man and the woman will feel the head of his penis "click" past the first ring of cartilage in her throat.

This will feel amazing for him, like he's really "gotten in there" for the first time...

Until then, it's just tight and "not complete..."

But once it gets in there it feels amazing for him.

For her it will feel scary – like she may not ever be able to get that dick out again!

It <u>will</u> come out!

Don't force her to keep it in there...

Let her stay in control of the situation, or you run the risk of scaring her away forever.

You <u>will</u> get back in there again! If you allow her to stay in control.

The woman must try to STAY RELAXED...

KEEP HER THROAT RELAXED...

STAY IN CONTROL...

MONITOR HER BREATHS...

Keep practicing!

The GAG REFLEX EVENTUALLY BECOMES CONTROLLABLE or MANAGEABLE.

If the woman really loves the man and wants to please him, wants to satisfy him, wants to make him feel totally accepted, she will experiment with positions and angles, and do whatever it takes to figure out how to deep throat him.

It can be advantageous to start deep throating him while his penis is soft, then to keep going as he gets harder and harder, to the point where you can't take it any more. Then continue working your way up, practicing, and becoming more skillful. Remember, Rome wasn't built in a day!

TIME YOUR BREATHING

Because the penis may be so large that it fills her entire throat, it may be difficult to breath, so it's important for the woman to get into a rhythm with her partner, breathing as she pulls out, so that she has enough air for when the penis is in her throat.

This is particularly important when the man is about to come. One thing many women don't know – even those who do deep throat – is that the most pleasurable thing for the man is to actually shoot into her throat. Which means that for this period of time you'll have to get by on the last breath you took prior to his ejaculation.

Women are not aware just how sensitive a man's penis can be during and just after ejaculation. Sucking is generally good for men as they're coming. Whereas continually bobbing up and down on the penis is not always pleasurable after ejaculation.

"DEEP TONGUE"
her G-spot

GREAT deep tongue is always sloppy.

The most important factor in deep tonguing:
Her level of arousal must be high.

When deep tonguing a woman who is highly aroused, her
G-spot will naturally shift position to facilitate contact with
his tongue.

HER ULTIMATE ORGASM
Many women experience their most intense
orgasmic climaxes when their clitoris
is licked and/or sucked while their G-spot is stimulated
to climax and/or ejaculation.

HIS ULTIMATE ORGASM(S)

Men can experience multiple ejaculations and extended continuous orgasms lasting many minutes if their penis is continuously sucked after ejaculation.

The woman should continue sucking (lightly at first, then harder as his passion remounts) after he reaches orgasm (and she swallows it.)

After a few minutes the sensation will become uncomfortable for him, and it is then that the man must force himself to let her keep sucking his penis. (I encourage the men who take my seminars to force themselves to let her keep sucking in the name of science!)

It may feel as if he is going to pee in her mouth, but that is impossible.

He must consciously decide to "let go," "go over the wall," and lose control to her mouth.

Once he surrenders to the intense pleasure, a man can experience multiple ejaculations and extended orgasms that last for many minutes.

The best way to learn this is for the man to lie flat on his back in a comfortable bed with the woman on top of him in 69.

Once a man learns how to access this level of sexuality, he can have these multiple orgasms and ejaculations anywhere. One of my students does it on Sunday evenings with his girlfriend in the Jacuzzi.

Both men and women can experience tremendous erotic pleasure from oral stimulation of the anus.

Bathing thoroughly prior to oral anal lovemaking is highly recommended.

Women especially enjoy oral stimulation of the entire vaginal-anal region.

Orally stimulating
a man's anus is a great way to "warm him up" for
"male sacred spot" massage (a.k.a. prostate massage.)

HOW TO MAKE LOVE TO AN ANUS
WITH YOUR MOUTH

Start by just breathing in the sweet scent of the freshly bathed anus – and breathing hot breaths on it as preparation for contact and preliminary arousal.

Then gently lick the buttocks and fine hairs around the anus.

Nibble and lick your lover's ass in concentric circles, getting closer and closer to the opening until you feel his or her intense desire for you to put your tongue inside.

If you do this teasingly and tantalizingly enough while also licking and sucking the vagina or penis (as the case may be) for the right amount of time, your partner will eventually be DYING for you to put your tongue inside.

This works great as a natural extension to a hot 69.

Only once you feel anal lust coming from your partner should you go for it.

Premature penetration of the anus may be uncomfortable for your lover to receive, and is certainly less than optimal when compared to expert timing.

Simultaneous oral-anal 69 can be amazing.
While modern medicine often advises
against intermixing vaginal and anal sex fluids, women
often go *crazy* with passion during the experience.

Orally stimulating her anus to the point of sexual frenzy
is a terrific prelude to anal intercourse – and a great way to
loosen a person up about the concept of anal sex. If you're
willing to "bite the bullet," she can't help being more
receptive to the idea of "taking a shot."

Great oral sex
does not require ejaculation.

BENEFITS OF DRINKING HIM
You get a nutritional, high-protein raw treat.
He will feel that you really care about and love him.

BENEFITS OF DRINKING AMRITA
Female ejaculate is said to have tremendous vitality
and transmits vital life force energy of the Goddess
to the lucky lover who drinks it.

FLAVOR
Some jizz tastes better than others.
Eating pineapple is said to sweeten a man's juices.
Deep throating him while he cums
will bypass your taste buds.

The flavor of female ejaculate
can vary from woman to woman
and sometimes from ejaculation to ejaculation.
It can taste salty or medicinal, like vanilla,
and even like Cap'n Crunch.

As amrita is a very elusive and ephemeral substance
only shared by extremely intimate lovers,
the drinker should feel honored by the very experience.

New Sex Advisor #66 © 2001 Clint & www.NewSex.org
Swallowing Is Not About Swallowing
   Fri, 15 Jun 2001 14:42:55 EDT
   From: Vgn124@aol.com
   Clint, hi, i'm 41 and my boyfriend is 48....i have done a lot
of things but swallowing isn't one of them...he wants me to...i
have tried a couple of times but can't...i've seen what it looks
like and i can't imagine swallowing it....or he'll ejaculate on
me and want me to lick the head...i want to get over this
problem cause he really wants me to do this...any ideas...i need
help... thank you.

   Dear Vgn,
   Swallowing is not about swallowing a substance; it's about
complete acceptance, wanting and loving everything about that
person. It's about completely letting a person in.
   What a man wants more than anything is complete
acceptance from a woman. That is what makes a man feel
loved.
   There are certain doors that remain closed until you've
accepted everything about a person – including their sexual
organs and ejaculate – inside and into your body. Until you
have, there is a limit to your intimacy.
   When you taste wine or other alcohols for the first time,
most people don't like the taste. After a while it becomes a
sought-after experience.
   When a person won't swallow, it's never about the taste.
   Swallowing is about accepting that liquid as a part of your
sexual interaction. About accepting everything about your man.
About loving everything that is him. If you won't swallow your

man's cum, you need to break up with him, because you really don't love him.

I have never been with a woman who loved me who refused to swallow.

Sincerely,

Your New Sex Advisor

New Sex Advisor #68 ©2001 Clint Arthur & www.NewSex.org
What She Likes About Swallowing
"There's something intense about feeling those contractions in your mouth, right in your face. You're really making it happen. You're really aware of all the phases that he's going through. It's very gratifying."

Have YOU tried New Sex™?

New Sex Advisor #69 ©2001 Clint Arthur & www.NewSex.org
New Sex™ with Cap'n Crunch
Our weekends are usually fantastic, but this Saturday went beyond our normal level of sensual euphoria.

Cheryl and I woke up ridiculously early in her big soft bed and cuddled for about forty-five minutes, trying to get back to sleep but not succeeding.

Then we had fresh juice and coffee with our favorite raw cream and Brazilian pepper tree honey – yummmmm! – and played a couple games of quickgammon (you use all four dice each time you roll…)

Then we took a shower and crawled back into bed, all clean and fresh…

And ready for some awesome deep-throat 69…

This woman has such an amazing attitude and skills to go with it…

And such yummy, clean-tasting snatch…

We spent a l-o-n-g time on our sides, gripping tight and sucking and slurping and swallowing each other to our mutual delight...

Then I started fingering her G-spot while I kept sucking her...

But in a 69 it's not really the right angle...

So I soon disentangled my cock from her throat...

And got my body between her spread legs...

Two-fingering her sacred spot intensely...

Then three fingers...

I know exactly how she likes it...

Pressing hard...

Then kind of pulsing with two fingers...

Alternating...

The fountain was quickly turned ON...

And it gushed...

And gushed...

Many times...

I watched the amrita collect magically in my open palm while my fingers worked their effect on her...

Then I leaned my mouth down to her hot heaven's gate...

And when I drank the ephemeral fluid...

It tasted intensely sweet...

I just couldn't place it...

"Please fuck me!" she screamed, cumming for like the sixth time...

I needed very little prodding in my animal sex frenzy...

Grabbing big handfuls of her ass, I pumped...

Deep and deeper inside her spread-wide-open love temple...

"I'm cumming again, I'm cumming again!" she moaned in delirium...

And as the hot, wet explosion and vaginal convulsions dazzled my rock hardness, I felt myself pulled directly over the edge, into a roaring orgasm…

With her cervix tweaking the head of my lingam…

Splash! Splash!

"Raaaaaaaaarrrrrrrrrgggggggggggghhhhhhhh!" I growled with a force I could not control…

It really surprised me how the sound HAD TO come out of my mouth…

And as we lay there catching our breath and sweating against each other's hot flesh, my mind whirred over that strangely familiar sweetness lingering on my taste buds…

Until at last the answer popped into my head…

It tasted just like Cap'n Crunch!

Sincerely,

Your New Sex Advisor

AN ACTUAL ORGY

A few weeks after shooting *Goddess Worship*, I had the privilege of being invited to Dr. Clarke's new apartment in Orange County for a *puja*, or worship.

In attendance were me, Dr. Clarke, her new twenty-four-year-old boyfriend Sean, her ex-boyfriend Evan, a fifty-something-year-old tantra master named Michael the Red, a really handsome Fire Dancer in his mid-twenties named Karl, a new and very buxom apprentice of Corynna's named Suzy, another young Goddess who was also an Internet personality going by the name Bathtub-girl, and an older blonde Goddess whom I had met during my search for a Love Goddess and who had been eliminated from the process because she was a tad too old. A few years earlier, she would have been a contender.

The older Goddess was the last to arrive, and as soon as she did, Corynna announced: "Everyone should partner up," and as I was standing right beside her, the older blonde Goddess asked if I would be her partner. I said, "I already have a partner."

I went over to Suzy and said, "You have to save me and be my partner."

She said, "I'd be honored to be your partner, Clint."

Everyone wore long, flowing wraps called sarongs around their waists. The women wore sexy bralike tops, Michael the Red had some kind of cool leather tantra-man vest, Sean, Karl, Evan, and I were bare-chested.

Corynna waved a handful of condoms in the air and said, "If anyone needs a condom at any time, there are plenty of them right here on this table. Now if everyone would please take their places in a large circle, we can get started."

As everyone was getting themselves into position, forming a large circle around the perimeter of the living room, Karl came over to where I was sitting beside Suzy and said to me, "You are a <u>warrior</u>. I <u>saw</u> myself with her." Then he nodded his head respectfully and walked away to sit beside the much older Goddess.

Michael the Red turned out to be a living legend in the tantra community, so Corynna asked him to lead the ceremony, and he said, "It would be my honor."

We began by all indulging in the sacraments which were graciously provided by our hostess: excellent marijuana, which we smoked from her bong, hits of Ecstasy for anyone who wanted, and shots of GHB.

Then we went around the circle, and everyone stated an intention.

Bathtub-girl was asked to speak first, and either she didn't quite understand the spirit of it all, or she was just SUCH a promoter that she used any opportunity that came her way to get the word out about Bathtubgirl.com. She stated her intention as "to keep doing her live webcast, spreading the message of love and free expression over the Internet, and continuing to be Bathtub-girl as much as possible." It was such a blatant commercial plug that I had to respect her for her commitment, even though it was out of place.

When it got to my turn, I stated my intention: "To continue straightening my spine, and to continue supporting the beauty and power of the Goddess."

When everyone had stated an intention, Michael the Red began a wild and outrageous incantation which I could never even hope to paraphrase – it was just SO of the moment – and it ended with a long flurry of semi-sung words in a language I had never heard before – as if he were speaking in tongues. Suzy later told me it had been Sanskrit.

After that, Corynna started chanting, and Sean, who was seated beside her, started banging a small ceremonial drum with a stick...

Bathtub-girl and Karl's Goddess started dancing in the middle of the circle...

Michael the Red picked up the chant and joined in the free-form, drug-hazy dance…

Even I started chanting along…

Buzzed as much from the thrill as from the drugs…

At some point Sean and Evan started "working on" Dr. Clarke's sacred spot in the middle of the living room floor…

Suzy and I started petting each other…

I'm not sure what the other people were doing, but there was always chanting and drumming and dancing going on…

Sometime later Dr. Clarke came over to me, took my hands in hers, looked into my eyes with her beautiful blues, and said, "Clint, may I honor your lingam?"

I said, "It would be my honor, oh Great One."

Then she dropped to her knees and started going down on me right in the middle of the living room floor.

It was the weirdest sensation, because I still was not the least bit physically attracted to her…

But I respected her as a great teacher, healer, and sexual powerhouse…

And so out of respect, I too honored her…

Dropping to my knees, and then onto my side…

And against my own better judgment, going down on her yoni…

So then there we were in a 69 in the middle of the floor…

Me and the Great One.

It was SO WEIRD…

Because I had sworn to myself that I would never have sex with Dr. Corynna Clarke…

I had told Goddess Natalia many times that I wasn't attracted to Corynna, and I would never be with her.

But Natalia had laughed at me…

She'd told me that I had no idea of the power I was dealing with…

That if Corynna wanted me or any man, she would have him.

And over and over I repeatedly stated I would never be attracted to Corynna...

Our 69 lasted ten minutes or so, and of course she gave really great, sloppy, saliva-thick, slurpy-sounding head...

Sucking deep and soft yet firm and satisfying...

Then when she was done with me, she pulled off, we looked into each other's eyes, and said "Namaste" – and she went back to her boyfriend and started having sex with him on the kitchen table.

I wandered into the bedroom and was pleased to find the buxom and sensual Goddess Suzy sprawled across Corynna's king-size bed.

Candles were burning, and the great Goddess music of Jillian Speer was wafting in from the living room.

I said, "Are you all right?"

She said, "I'm wonderful, just very buzzed."

I said, "Let me give you a massage, Goddess."

She said, "Thank you, that would be lovely."

I started rubbing the Goddess's shoulders and neck, using slightly more than pure sensual pressure...

Stimulating the blood to flow through her muscles...

Working my way down her back, I asked, "May I unhook your bra?"

She nodded.

I undid the clasp, and began massaging down her spine...

Working the muscles of her lower back with my strong fingers...

Gently massaging the base of her spine and the crack of her ass with my raging erection...

Her hips began to move in a sexy, wavelike motion...

And I undid her sarong to bare her butt...

To massage it with my fingers...

To gnaw on her heated flesh with my mouth...

Massaging her buttocks and thighs...

Seeing her back begin to arch with mounting arousal...

I lay down on her back and turned her head to kiss her...

Our mouths met and opened readily for dancing tongues...

Her legs spread and I entered her from behind...

So natural...

Two beings sharing energy of love...

<u>Not trying to come...</u>

<u>Just being together...</u>

<u>Just getting to know each other...</u>

<u>Exploring the sexual energy of another person...</u>

Riding a wave of sensual and chemical buzz together...

Without any judgments...

No agendas...

Just exploration and being...

Just enjoying the pleasure of sexual union with an equally high-level and sophisticated "player."

Sometime later, Karl came into the room and said, "I hope I'm not disturbing you..."

I said, "Not at all."

Suzy said, "There's plenty of room – it's a big bed."

Karl got onto the bed, and as I continued pumping into her from behind, she crawled forward on her elbows and began to honor Karl's lingam.

The guy was in heaven!

Suzy has such a big, beautiful mouth...

Such strong lips...

An amazing tongue...

And with the force of my thrusts propelling her deep into a sexual bliss state, she really let go and got into the rhythm and the ritual of her sucking.

It was incredible to watch the effect of it on him and on her.

And I lowered myself down onto her back so I could get my head as close as possible to her mouth…

So I could really get in there and watch…

This CLOSE-UP, live sex show…

It was AMAZING…

She was taking all of his length and girth with such ease, control, mastery, skill, and sensual grace…

In and out…

Deep and wet…

Cupping his balls…

Sucking and slurping…

I was enthralled with it…

Suddenly she took a hold of his lingam with her left hand, pulled it out of her mouth and pointed it at me with a look like, *Do you want to suck it for a while?*

Karl was a gorgeous man…

In great shape from his work as a professional fire dancer…

His penis was rock hard and right in my face…

But I didn't have even the slightest bit of desire to suck it, him, or any man.

Not then, not now, not ever.

I just shook my head like, *No thank you,* and she went right back to sucking him for several minutes longer.

She was so into it!

We all were.

I started pounding her from behind with force and depth.

Karl started pumping his penis into her mouth, really working it…

And in a few minutes she was groaning and moaning and convulsing with orgasmic pleasure and delight…

I think she came, but she didn't ejaculate, so I can't say for sure.

All I know is that a great time was had by all…

EVEN THOUGH NOBODY SEEMED TO HAVE AN ORGASM.

The EXPERIENCE was what it was about…

NOT CUMMING…

JUST DOING IT.

Some time around 3:30 Karl thanked us both and left.

Then I lay down on my back and moaned with frazzled delight as the Goddess Suzy went down and began honoring me.

I said, "I don't want to cum."

She said, "Why not?"

I said, "Men are supposed to save their seed, to keep their power."

She said, "You're a great man, Clint. You deserve it. I want you to come. I want you to come in my mouth. I want to drink you. I want to honor you like that. And I want you to honor me like that."

Then there was no more talk.

I just lay there on my back as she rubbed her big luscious breasts on my shaft and on my balls…

And she sucked me deep and full and wet and hard and built to a slow, steady, perfectly controlled, super-expert climax…

And as I shot my potent power-seed, she sucked me all the way to the base of my shaft…

Squeezing the entire length of my cock with her tongue and her mouth muscles and her lips and her Goddess energy…

And I felt that as deep as I could go, she could take it all, every drop, every inch, every electron of energy and more…

The Great Goddess was paying me back for my faithful and honest devotion…

This was a gift from her.

INSIDE THE GODDESS TEMPLE

One of the best parts of being an instructor at the Learning Annex is having the opportunity to attend any of the other classes for free.

One of the best ones that I took was a class on Manifesting Career Breakthroughs, with a man named Paul Roth. Paul was in his early fifties, with intense, penetrating blue eyes, and a striking resemblance to Winston Churchill.

I signed on for additional work with Paul at his Institute for Applied Ontology, and it was during my first sixteen-week program geared toward complete Life Transformation that I came up against a major hurdle in my life plan for success.

Paul asked, "Why aren't you in a relationship right now?"

I said, "It's a conscious decision. I decided that I wouldn't get into a serious relationship again until I 'made it.' "

"So you're going to stay alone, all by yourself, until you attain some concept of success that you've determined for yourself, is that right?"

I said, "Yeah. I'm gonna make it, or I'm gonna die trying to make it."

"I've got news for you," he said. "Unless you get into a relationship with a woman, you will die trying. You will never make it."

I asked, "Why is that?"

He said, "Women are better than us. They tolerate us. And if you get the right woman, she'll teach you, inspire you, guide you, and make you a better man. I've been married three times, and each time I learned and grew and became more than I was before getting into the relationship. If it wasn't for those women, I could never have been the man I am today."

I was paying $500 a month for this program. I was still driving a cab on weekends to pay my bills. Sales of *New Sex Now* were only trickling in off my website. I wanted desperately to change and break through to prosperity, and I was committed to doing whatever was necessary. Paul was my "Coach" in charge of orchestrating this transformation. I trusted him, and agreed to make a conscious effort to get into a relationship with a strong woman.

I started by calling up my ex-girlfriends, women I had shared brief liaisons with, seeing if there was any interest, if they knew of anyone who fit the profile of the woman I was looking for.

Then late one night in December, I was talking with Dr. Clarke on the phone. She was depressed. She and Sean had broken up. She had broken off her engagement to Charles Muir and canceled her Christmas–New Year trip to Maui. It was a Friday night, and New Year's Eve fell on Sunday. She was all alone in her new apartment in Orange County, depressed, and despairing at her empty future…

My mind started whirring through the possibilities and the ramifications. At this point, she was my good friend, we were working together on the Goddess Worship project, and we had a whole series of Sacred Sex and Tantra videos planned. I didn't want to screw up the prospects of producing all those Goddess-themed videos by getting into a personal relationship with her. Personal relationships in the entertainment business ALWAYS spelled DOOM for working relationships.

On the other hand, she was, in my estimation, one of the most powerful Goddesses in Southern California, and possibly in the world. If I did get into a relationship with her, the potential for personal education, edification, enlightenment, and empowerment would be immense.

Here she was, for this brief moment in time, unattached.

I remember my mind trying frantically to process all this as I was talking to her on the phone. I knew that she was into me – she had told me several times that I was high up on her "list of men I want to have sex with." And she had made a big point of telling Suzy how jealous she was of her Karl-n-Clint Sandwich.

After about five minutes of weighing the pros and cons, I decided to seize the moment of opportunity. I said, "Great One, may I have the honor of coming to your apartment and spending the weekend with you?"

She said, "Oh, Clint! Are you sure?"

I said, "Some of the very best times of my entire year were with you. I'm sure that if we were together this weekend, it would be the best possible time I could have."

She said, "Okay then. But I'm warning you – I've just been depressed and lying in bed for three days. I look like shit."

I made the drive down to Orange County in record time.

When I got there the door was unlocked, and I entered to find her in bed, with a single candle burning. She was drunk and dirty.

The first thing I did was to run a hot bubble bath and make a pot of green tea. Then I carried her into the bathroom, and gently lowered her into the tub.

I washed her entire body with a soft cloth and pleasantly scented bath gel...

I washed her hair, and made sure to give her a beautiful, relaxing, therapeutic scalp massage in the process...

The whole time she kept looking at me with those intense blue eyes...

It was a look filled with amazement and gratitude...

And love...

I rinsed her off in the shower, then patted her dry with several fluffy towels...

Then I asked her, "Do you want to pee?"

While she did, I changed the bed sheets and lit another candle...

Then I undressed and we both lay down in her big purple canopy bed...

Just me and the Great One...

Staring into each other's eyes...

Slowly, for the very first time, I leaned forward to kiss her...

She lay there waiting to receive me...

Gently parted her lips...

And our mouths connected.

This was a kiss completely different from any I had ever shared.

HER TONGUE WAS COMPLETELY SOFT AND RELAXED.

Her mouth was a pool of tenderness and compassion...

And her blue eyes never left my own.

I can't believe I'm kissing the Great One, I thought. *Wow!*

I said, "Thank you for honoring me with your lips."

She just looked at me in amazement.

My devotion and respect were completely sincere, despite her debilitated condition on this evening.

I saw her for the greatness that she was...

The vast storehouse of knowledge of the sexual arts...

Her leadership and preeminence in the Goddess community...

I was soaking up everything about these moments.

Our kisses were slow, unhurried, a true master dance of tongues.

I continued by breathing on her nipples, and making soft circles around them with my fingertips...

Then I looked into her eyes and asked, "May I honor your yoni, Great One?"

She slowly nodded her ascent...

Then she said, "We should put some towels under me first. They're at the side of the bed."

I reached down and found a stack of towels. I placed two of them under her hips; then I moved between her legs and used every technique for slow, sensuous pleasure I could call to use…

When I think about being present in the moment, I go back to that night and reflect on it in wonder!

Breathing on her vagina…

Licking around the lips in soft, slow circles…

Licking up one lip and down the other…

Circling around her clitoris…

Softly flicking it…

Then taking it between my lips and gently sucking…

Moving it in and out between my lips while flicking my tongue…

Engorging it with blood…

Taking both her lips in my mouth, sucking them…

Licking up between them with my tongue…

And all this time she was watching me…

And I was maintaining eye contact with her…

Until finally I paused and asked, "Great One, may I enter your temple?"

She slowly nodded…

And with her clitoris softly sucked between my lips I gently, slowly licked two fingers…

And softly slid them into her yoni temple…

Up and around her pubic bone…

Until I felt the roughness and ridges of her sacred Goddess spot.

I held my fingers there motionless for a long time as she moaned a long and sensual "Ooooooooooohhhhhhhhhhhhhhh."

I echoed that sound with a long "Aaaaaaaaaaahhhhhhhhh."

Then I gently started tapping on her Goddess spot…

Ever so softly and slowly…

And began to feel the ridges smoothing out…

Using more pressure, I started pressing…

Then sliding my fingers in and out…

Circling...

Swooshing her cervix...

I moved up to lie beside her and hold her with my other arm...

As we kissed and kept eye contact, I hugged her firmly to let her know that I was there with her and that she was in the arms of a competent, caring lover...

Her moans and Ooooooohs and Ahhhhs grew and grew...

My own sounds of sharing pleasure flowed freely, and I vocalized emotions and arousal with her as never before...

Moving through the precursory stages of female ejaculation, I soon felt the pre-ejaculatory flood-rush...

And then she began to flow!

With great gushes...

Prodigious splashes of amrita soaked through the towels in mere minutes...

Then I moved my hips between her legs and entered her with my lingam...

I was VISUALIZING my penis hitting her G-spot...

And I became amazed as I circled her sacred spot with the head of my penis.

We shared this sacred union for a thousand strokes...

And I felt the rush of her ejaculations and orgasms several times on and around me...

But the idea of my release was out of the question...

I still had a long way to go...

Turning her over onto her knees I entered her from behind and delivered another thousand strokes...

Then, finally, at around 3:30 in the morning, I put her back into missionary and pumped away until she flooded yet again...

And very consciously I allowed myself to relax with satisfaction...

Pulling out at the last moment to spew my seed all over her belly.

She looked at me like I was a bit crazy…

But I didn't care – I had showed up strong for our first night together; I was tired and frazzled and needing sleep…

Which came to me at once when I lay down beside her and said, "I love you, Great One."

She said, "I love you, Clint."

LESSONS FROM THE GREAT ONE

By the end of New Year's weekend, I was officially Dr. Corynna Clarke's New Boyfriend, and well on my way toward learning some very powerful and very difficult lessons about love and sexual energy.

1) Oral sex should be sloppy and slurpy and loud. She gave excellent head, and the primary reason it was so good was that her blowjobs were so SLOPPY and SALIVARY. And she always made loud, slurpy sucking sounds to stimulate me with auditory sensations. I started making those sloppy slurpy sounds with my abundant saliva when I gave her head too, with excellent results.

2) Yin & Yang: While men feel good about themselves for being very Yang, very strong, very tough, and macho, women don't always enjoy that hardness. Dr. Clarke most often encouraged me to be soft, gentle, tender, more "feminine" – more Yin. I am not at all trying to say that manly power and force is bad during sex – just that demonstrating and using Yin abilities is a great thing for a man to do too.

3) We would make love for hours at a time, and one night on my boat I created what I call the "Start-and- Stop

Technique" – which really impressed her. It's very simple yet very powerful. All you do is stop pumping during sexual intercourse, yet remain together. For example, I'd be on top of her in missionary position, pumping and pumping, then I'd stop and just lie on top of her, petting her, kissing her, still inside her. Then after a minute or two I'd start pumping again for a few minutes, then I'd stop again and relax with her, then start up and stop, over and over.

4) Sexual Massage: She was lying on her stomach one time during a doggy-style session, and I started massaging her back while I was pumping into her. I used my hands, my elbows, my forearms, my chin, my cheeks, my hair – everything I could think of to <u>give her a sensual and yummy massage during our lovemaking</u>. She LOVED it.

5) An erection is not mandatory for intimate contact between lovers. She sometimes would get mad at me when I would get an erection during fellatio. She often preferred sucking my penis while it was flaccid.

6) Women do not need to have orgasms every time they have sex. They enjoy the closeness and intimacy as much as anything else. Men also have this capacity, but it requires development.

JEALOUSY

We invited Evan over to spend New Year's Eve with us, and while he was giving her sacred spot massage, I was videotaping them, she was maintaining eye contact with me, and I said, "Say 'I love Clint.' "

That was kind of a fucked thing for me to say, seeing how she and Evan used to be live-in boyfriend and girlfriend, but I wanted to hear it, and she said it. I wasn't jealous of him because I knew she loved me now.

But the issue of jealousy was by no means put to rest.

To her, love was love, separate from sex, almost unconnected.

We went to the Internext Adult Webmaster convention together in Las Vegas the first week of January, and as I walked around with her on the convention floor, it was as if all the traffic lights were green.

People I couldn't get to meet before, now, in the presence of the Goddess, were saying "Yes."

We met Danni Ashe, and attended a private party at her mega-suite in the Four Seasons Hotel, then I took us out to an expensive dinner at the Top of the World restaurant high above Las Vegas in the crown of the Stratosphere. It was a dreamy time, everything was simple, and I was ON.

Then we went to a huge webmaster party at the Stage 16 mega-nightclub, and she started going down on me while I was standing at the bar, drinking a beer. It was dark, and a very low-key situation because of that, but some black guy spied what was going on, started laughing, and high-fived me.

A short time later she came up for air, put my erection back into my pants, and zipped up my fly. The guy behind her at the bar turned to her and said something, and then they started making out. I didn't really mind it, until it kept going on and on and on.

I stepped away from the bar and stood apart from them, watching my girlfriend kissing this complete stranger, and I began to really get bothered. Not because she was kissing some guy, but because she was ignoring me for so long.

Finally they stopped kissing and she gave him her email address. I took her by the hand and led her out of the party.

"I almost walked out on you back there," I said as we walked through the Venetian Casino.

"Really? Why?"

"Because you were ignoring me."

She said, "I'm sorry, Clint. I didn't mean to upset you. I was just building up shakti for you."

Later that week, back in California, I went over to her house one night, and while we were making love, while I was INSIDE HER, she said, "Today, when I was fucking my client in the Healing Room, I just couldn't stop thinking of you."

I immediately lost my erection, and rolled off her.

She said, "What's wrong, Clint?"

I said, "I know you have sex with other people, and that's fine. I just don't want to hear about it while I'm actually fucking you."

She said, "But Clint, every single moment that I was with him, I was only thinking about you, and about bringing all that shakti back to you tonight. No one can replace the connection that we have and that I feel for you. No matter who may be fucking me, there's only one Clint."

I said, "That's fine. Just please don't tell me about it while I'm fucking you."

Intellectually it made sense. Emotionally it was difficult for me at the time.

Only now that I am in such a profound and committed relationship with Cheryl do I fully understand what Corynna was talking about. When I think about the idea of having sex with other women, or even having a ménage with Cheryl and another woman, it doesn't even make sense that I would get any satisfaction out of having sex with another woman. Sure, I could probably DO IT, but the natural connection that I share with Cheryl is what makes our lovemaking so fulfilling.

REVIEW QUIZ

1.   For some people, oral sex is _____ intimate than sexual intercourse.

2.   What a woman wants from oral sex: _____ and _____.

3.   Great oral sex is often _____ and _____ and _____.

4.   _____ allows both partners to give and receive.

5.   _____ and _____ of oral lovemaking can be the greatest thrill.

6.   List three positions for 69.

7.   Many women enjoy sucking a flaccid _____ as much as or more than an erect one.

8.   The least effective position for going down on someone is _____.

9.   Great deep throat and great deep tongue are always _____ and _____.

10.   Gag reflex during deep throat will eventually be mastered if the woman _____ ___ _____.

11.   Great sex does not require _____.

12.   Describe the "Start-and- Stop Technique."

7
ANAL PLEASURES

> *"It has been found that, in most marriages, it's the woman who controls the diversity of the couple's repertoire – and in a sense, the frequency of sexual relations, because the more diversified the lovemaking practices, the more frequent the lovemaking."*
> *-Dr. Joyce Brothers.*

Anal sex is vital to any healthy relationship. Three reasons:

1) As Dr. Joyce Brothers' quote above implies, variety is not just the spice of life, but one of the keys to a healthy sex life.

2) It's fun! I'm a Virgo, so believe me when I tell you I had a huge hang-up about anal sex before I gave in and allowed Natalia to shove her tongue where no tongue had ever gone before. But I was quickly converted to the gospel of the growler gourmet! It is very intimate, requires a huge amount of trust and vulnerability, and a whole new experience if you've never done it before. Both women and men report having orgasms from anal sex. One of my girlfriends told me she was ADDICTED to it for a long time, and always enjoyed multiple orgasms from our anal adventures. Gay guys and tantra Goddesses swear by the power of a penis or probing finger up the poop chute for male pleasure *par excellence,* especially during fellatio. For women, a finger inserted in there during sexual intercourse adds yet another exciting variable into the mix that excites and stimulates.

3) In most male-female relationships, it's vital for the man to be "in charge," sexually and otherwise. Every dog pack has an Alpha dog. The Alpha leader does whatever he wants to any member of the pack, and if

they don't like it, they leave. I believe the same is true for human relations. The man should do whatever he wants to with the woman, and demonstrate his position of dominance sexually. I'm not saying that he should inflict pain or suffering on her. His skill level should provide him ready and willing access to every orifice of her body, including her ass. Anal sex allows her to fully surrender to him. It's equally vital for a woman to be able to submit to his domination and control in a way that is only available through anal sex. Anal submission creates vulnerability that can open vast new territories of intimacy for the couple. Submission also requires trust. Giving trust begets more trust, and more intimacy, and more honest bonding between the man and woman.

New Sex Advisor # 23 ©2001 Clint Arthur & www.NewSex.org
How to Fuck Her Tight-Puckered Ass
Clint,

What can you advise my wife and me in anal sex? She can handle her toys, but when it comes to mine she puckers up tight.

She says "it's too big," but compared to some of the toys I use at the same time it's about even. I think it's that she visualizes the size of her toys and she sees them as two units, not one, and mine as just big. Can this be the case? She has no trouble receiving them, she likes it, but when it comes to mine, "too big."

Help!

Gonzo and Pam

Dear Gonzo,

The other night was truly something special.

Cheryl and I have been seeing each other for about two months now.

Great sex (bareback despite her semivirginal health-conscious attitude); vaginal yes, oral yes, yet prior to Sunday, nothing anal.

But that night I did the New Sex™ Techniques on her fully from Step 1 right through to the end, by the book, and something very interesting happened.

While anal sex is not normally part of the process, as I was implementing the physical techniques, I unexpectedly started fucking her in the ass for the very first time!

Surprised the hell out of both of us!

But my dick went in with NO LUBRICANT and NO TROUBLE AT ALL.

This was particularly surprising to her because (she told me the next morning): "The other couple of times you tried to get in there it was NOT HAPPENING AT ALL – I was totally closed up tight, and I was worried that you would be too big for anal sex." (Supposedly, she's only had anal sex with two other men.)

I only did it for a few strokes – maybe ten – because I'm not so much into anal sex when I can have New Sex™, so I ended up pulling out of her ass, then I had her blow me for a few minutes, then I gave her a long series of ejaculations using my fingers to stimulate her G-spot, and then I put on a condom and we had sexual intercourse that climaxed with simultaneous ejaculations – what I call the New Sex™ Experience.

She got EXTREMELY FUCKING WILD THAT NIGHT.

So did I.

I mean, it was some of the most ANIMAL-INTENSE, GROWLING, SWEATY SEX I've EVER had.

I bet the short anal interlude had something to do with it, and I'll definitely be back in there for more taboo-tightness soon – especially since she can't get pregnant that way and I'm SO DYING TO SHOOT A non-condomized load inside her.

Now, I don't really consider myself an expert on anal sex, but in my opinion as just a guy who got to fuck his new girlfriend in the ass for the first time despite what seemed to be a very tight-puckered situation, the key to getting in there was doing all the New Sex™ Techniques to produce <u>Trust, Relaxation, Desire, and Presence in the Moment,</u> and most importantly, creating an intense level of AROUSAL.

Without a doubt, the thing I did that turned her on the most – and turned ME on the most too! – was this: When she was on her stomach, during the Ultimate Erotic Massage phase of the techniques, I was doing the "Breath on her Vagina Technique," then I started eating her box, and then I started eating her ass.

If you want to be guaranteed to be able to fuck a woman's ass, you have to eat that ass.

Chow down, baby!

If you eat a woman's ass and she gets into it, fucking that ass will be the next logical step.

I'm not talking about a woman who let's you grab a little lick in there – I'm talking about a chick who sticks her ass up in the air and pushes her butt cheeks back into your face, moaning with delight as you bury your tongue in her anus. That chick will love it when you fuck her ass.

Cheryl was just tossing her head back and forth on the pillow, not protesting one bit, just moaning with pleasure, and the only thing she said was, "Just take it easy, okay?"

I'm telling you, once I dipped in there and started to stroke, she was ready for me to take a long hard RIDE!

And I will soon, I assure you that.

Also, even though experts like Charles Muir tell you not to mix butt-munching with pussy-eating, I get tremendous results when I feast on the entire pelvic area – going up and down, eating pussy and ass all during the same session.

So get down there and feast, and please write back to let us all know how it works out! You have a responsibility to the community to share your experiences and the benefits of my expertise! We'll all much appreciate it.

Sincerely,

Your New Sex™ Advisor

GUARANTEED PAIN-FREE ANAL SEX

The other night we were in the Jacuzzi and I tried to have anal sex with Cheryl, but it was no go. Too tight.

So I gave her several G-spot orgasms and ejaculations with my fingers and then tried anal penetration again.

This time she was wide open for business. Several subsequent repeat performances have proven the effectiveness of this surefire technique and guarantor of pain-free anal sex.

DOUBLE GODDESS VALENTINES

For Valentine's Day Dr. Clarke arranged for us to drive down to Baja, Mexico, for an overnight party with her good friend Goddess Laurel, a very busty, perky brunette with a fresh, cool attitude, and years of tantra experience.

I picked Laurel up at her home in West L.A., and we drove down to Corynna's house in my Bronco. Then the three of us drove to Ensenada in Corynna's BMW.

She had brought some weed, but the girls both wanted to stop at a *pharmacía* in Tijuana to pick up additional supplies: Valium, Percocet, and Vicodin.

Not being a drug addict or pill popper myself, I had no idea what I was in for or what was really going on. And I had no idea how much stuff they bought until we checked into our hotel room and they started popping pills and gloating over their huge new stash.

You see, here's the thing: I am glad to "party" with alcohol and certain "low key" drugs. But I'm an Ivy League graduate, not a junkie. And I'll never allow myself to become one.

There were two of them there for my total indulgence and amusement, so even though Corynna was pretty zonked out, I still had a ton of fun sexual indulgence with Laurel. And by the end of this minitrip they had decided to take a work expedition to Miami together, and invited me to join them.

One of the big video chains I'd sold *Goddess Worship* to had inquired about Gay Tantra videos. The president of that company had said, "We would do HUGE numbers for you on any Gay Tantra titles you could send us." Miami seemed like a perfect place to find cheap talent for a production about Gay Tantra. Corynna said she'd love to direct a Gay Tantra video, so I accepted and began preparing to produce my first gay movie during our ten days in Miami.

I didn't know it at the time, but that trip would be a major turning point in my life.

EMOTIONAL RESERVOIR

We arrived in Miami and checked into a suite at the Alexander Hotel, a huge, expensive condo and resort hotel complex right on the beach. They gave us a great place on one of the top floors with ocean views for miles, and gigantic beds.

That night I was in the master suite with Corynna, massaging her sacred spot, when I was confronted by something I had no way of expecting or preparing for.

All of sudden she started wailing and crying and moaning…

It was kind of like how she was regularly…

Very vocal…

Making very animal-like sounds…

But this was starting to get a bit different…

She was fighting against me…

And as she struggled, my natural instinct had me keep her in my physical control, to keep stimulating her G-spot…

Soon she was ejaculating with a huge gush…

But she was also screaming and crying!

Screaming SO LOUD that I started kissing her mouth just to stifle the sounds of her screams…

Ultimately she kept screaming and screaming and struggling against me, so I let her go, and when she calmed down about ten notches, I asked, "What happened?"

She said, "I was reliving when I was twelve years old, and my father was raping me."

I said, "I'm sorry; I had no idea."

She kept crying, hugging herself, not looking at me, looking up at the ceiling, and then she said, "When you were shoving your tongue in my mouth, I kept tasting the taste of my father's cum."

That really freaked me out.

I stayed with her, just lying next to her, for about fifteen more minutes, then I went out into the living room of the suite. Goddess Laurel was sitting at the desk pretending to be busy on her laptop computer.

She said, "What the hell was going on in there? I'm afraid somebody's gonna call the police!"

"She said when I was doing her sacred spot that she was having a flashback to when her father was raping her."

"Oh…," Goddess Laurel said, with puzzle pieces clearly coming together in her mind. "That makes a lot of sense. The Goddess spot is the repository for all kinds of emotional wounds, especially sexual abuse issues like rape and incest. That stuff stays trapped in there until one day it comes out – if a woman's lucky enough to have someone who can access it with her and for her."

"It freaked the shit out of me," I stammered. "I didn't know what to do! I tried to make her stop screaming, but she wouldn't. I tried to hold her but she pushed me away. I stayed with her, but then I just had to leave."

"You did exactly what you were supposed to do, Clint. All you <u>could</u> do was be with her as much as she would let you. She never told you about that before?"

"No, I never knew anything about this. I thought the G-spot was just good times."

"It's a very powerful gateway and energy source. Usually it's just good, but sometimes terrible shit can come out of it. I'm proud of you, Clint. You did good."

Just then Corynna erupted with terrifying shouts from the bedroom. "Will whoever's on my fucking phone line get the fuck off!"

It sounded as if the Devil had taken possession of Dr. Corynna Clarke. Laurel and I looked at each other with shock widening our eyes.

"God fucking dammit! I want to use the fucking phone! Unplug the fucking computer!"

Laurel quickly yanked the cord, and then we exchanged more perplexed looks in silence.

This was the beginning of Dr. Clarke's complete transformation into Miss Hyde, a totally abusive, irrational, combative, jittery, emotionally fragile monster liable to lash out with words or fists or manic tantrums at any moment.

I ended up moving out of Dr. Clarke's suite and sleeping on the extra bed in Goddess Laurel's room. By the seventh day in Miami I had stopped having sex with Corynna, had broken up two fistfights between her and Laurel, had watched her plow through a few cases of Budweiser, all the Valium, Xanax, and marijuana in the suite, had bonded in combat-based friendship with Laurel, and had realized that Corynna's emotional issues probably had as much to do with alcohol as they did drugs.

I contacted Dr. Hyla Kass, the tantra community shrink, and discussed the issue with her. I also called up a good friend of mine who worked in the drug-alcohol recovery field, and spoke with him about how to get her dried out. He and I made arrangements to get her checked into a facility upon our return to L.A. Then I called Corynna's mother to discuss the situation with her, so that she could make arrangements to keep up payments on the BMW and the apartment.

Then I went in and talked with Corynna about her situation.

She was totally on edge, and the slightest misstep or misspoken word would set her off into a trembling fit or intense screaming episode.

I said, "Corynna, you need to get help. You need to dry out, and get off the drugs and alcohol."

She said, "I know. But I can't do it. I've tried. I've tried many times, but I can't stop."

I said, "You've got to do it once and for all. I've talked to a friend who can get you into a clinic you can afford."

She screamed, "I'm not going into some fucking free clinic with a bunch of fucking crack whores!"

"Corynna, whatever the place is, you've got to break free of this dependence on drugs and liquor."

"I know, I know. Please help me."

"When you get back to L.A., I'm going to check you into this clinic."

She said, "Thank you."

The next morning – the day before Corynna was scheduled to fly back to L.A. with me and get checked into a clinic, I woke up to the sounds of banging across the suite. Corynna was packing her bags, getting ready to bug out of Miami.

I said, "What's going on?"

She said, "My mother says you're trying to be my pimp and control my life. I'm flying home in two hours."

I said, "Corynna, the boys are coming to shoot the Gay Tantra video this afternoon. You're supposed to direct it."

She said, "You'll figure something out. I'm taking my lights and my camera; pack them up in their cases for me."

I said, "I was relying on using your lights and camera for the shoot."

She said, "You've got your own camera."

I said, "Corynna, what are you doing? You need help."

She said, "You don't want to help me; you just want to control me."

By now Laurel had come into the living room to see what all the ruckus was about. She said, "Corynna, we love you; we just want to help you."

Corynna started crying and screamed, "If you want to fucking help me, then fucking pack up the fucking lights and get out my fucking way!"

A few minutes later the bellman came for her bags. Crying, she hugged me good-bye and said, "I didn't want to hurt you."

I said, "Take care of yourself, Corynna."

Then she hugged Laurel goodbye and said, "Sorry for being so mean to you."

Laurel said, "Get help, Corynna. We love you."

Corynna was sobbing, and Laurel started crying, and Corynna walked out the door and slammed it behind her. This was so surreal – the whole thing seemed like a scene straight out of *Clean & Sober*.

You could immediately feel the tension dissipate from the apartment.

The issue was crystal clear for me. Being Corynna's man required total worship of the Goddess. Being who she is, and what she is, and considering all the "perks" of being her lover, many men would gladly jump at the chance to dedicate their life to serving her.

But my life, my goals, my ambitions, my hopes and dreams were and always will be important to me. I don't expect that I'll ever willingly subjugate them to anyone else's life.

So Corynna went on with her life, and I went on with mine, seeking out a great sexual relationship with a woman who respected me and what I was about, and whose person, goals, and life I respected equally. Turned out she was waiting for me when I got back to Los Angeles, in the curvy, womanly, traditional form of my sexy, sweet little vixen, Cheryl.

Meanwhile, the boys showed up at the marble Miami penthouse an hour later. I shot and directed the video. Laurel told the guys what to do and how to breathe, and basically choreographed the entire experience for them, including the male sacred spot massage and how to move the energy all the way up through the seven chakras.

The astounding point for me was how the Gay Tantra experience was essentially the same as the Goddess Worship experience.

I learned that just like women, men have a sacred spot – located a few inches up the rectal passage. It also feels like a rough area on otherwise smooth walls. Laurel described it as being like the shape of an almond.

Stimulation of the male sacred spot during fellatio leads to massive whole-body sacred orgasms for the man. And by vocalizing the orgasmic sensations while visualizing the movement of energy up through the chakras, all seven sexual energy centers become activated and energized by the experience, and ultimately the energy explodes out of the crown chakra at the top of the head, and into the universe.

The results of a Gay Tantra experience are more intimacy and bonding for the participants, with a much more intense and honest connection. Sex becomes a sacred expression of affection, care, and shared closeness.

Of course, women can use this knowledge to stimulate their man's sacred spot during fellatio too. Cheryl often works one of her fingers up to and into my rectum as I approach climax during one of her deep-throat masterpieces, and the effect is erotically thrilling.

On the plane ride back to L.A., I continued discussing tantra with Goddess Laurel, and began to really understand that in Sacred Sexuality a triangle is formed between the two lovers and their higher power. The sacred spot – the release point for the most potent sexual energy – is the gateway to God.

Laurel said, "Humans and all animals have one primary purpose, and that is to reproduce. The natural energy needed to create life during reproduction is the most powerful natural force on earth. Every time we turn that power on, we are turning on the power of creation, the power of God. That's why everyone loves sex – because we thrill with that power. It's when you learn how to use that power that you can really make things happen."

"How do you use that power?" I wondered aloud.

Gazing out the window at 36,000 feet of blue sky, she whispered, "Sex Magic."

<u>REVIEW QUIZ</u>

1. The more _____ the lovemaking practices, the more frequent the lovemaking.

2. Guaranteed pain-free anal sex is accomplished by first giving the woman several _____ orgasms and _____.

3. The "Goddess spot" is the repository for all kinds of _____ wounds.

4. The "male sacred spot" is located a few inches up the _____.

5. The natural energy needed to create life during sexual reproduction is the _____ powerful energy force known on earth.

6. By vocalizing and visualizing the movement of energy up through the chakras, all __ energy centers become _____.

7. Many women _____ simultaneous stimulation of the vagina and anus.

8. Many men _____ simultaneous stimulation of the penis and anus.

9. The best way to "warm up" an anus for sexual penetration is with your _____.

8
SEX MAGIC

MANIFESTING DREAMS INTO REALITY

I spent many months studying and reading about Sex Magic in books and on the Internet before finally gaining the inspiration to do my first Sex Magic ceremony with another person after watching the movie *Spiderman*.

Some people think it's evil to pervert the natural power of sexual energy to one's own design or purpose. Others recognize the positive impact that benevolent use of such powers can have on humanity and the world at large.

Personally, I was a bit intimidated and embarrassed to begin practicing Sex Magic with someone else. But I knew that in order to really gain the most power from my relationship with Cheryl, I needed to enroll her into my Sex Magic program. Hopefully, to our mutual benefit.

Margo Anand, in her excellent book *The Art of Sexual Magic*, explains that while basic ceremonies and Sex Magic "devices" can be of use when designing one's own ceremonies and practices, ultimately a magician must teach him/herself how to be a magician.

It was during a scene in *Spiderman* where the hero learns how to use his magic spider-web power that I really understood the truth of what Margo Anand was saying. It was a funny sequence where Spiderman keeps experimenting with his wrists to try to get the web to shoot out. And only after many trials and errors does he finally gain control over this power to the point where he can make it work at will.

That was a perfect metaphor for where I was and were I needed to go with Sex Magic. I just had to get into it and figure it out until I could make it work.

Here is the basic concept behind Sex Magic:

1) According to Tony Robbins and many others, humans move toward pleasure and away from pain.

2) It's widely recognized across various disciplines in the self-help movement that whatever your subconscious mind

believes to be true will be manifested into your reality. How exactly this happens will vary from case to case. This is along the lines of visualization, only on a much deeper level.

So, with Sex Magic, essentially what you do is you powerfully anchor a desire or goal in your subconscious mind by repeatedly visualizing it during sex. Then you give that goal an extra shot of positive energy by turbo-charging it with the force of an orgasm.

The key to the entire process is BELIEF. You need to believe that whatever you wish to manifest is already actually in existence.

From my studies and experiences, it seems that Sex Magic is most effective at manifesting changes in personality or character traits. The rationale for this is that if you want to change your world, you have to change yourself. Once you are BEING the person that you want to become, then you'll automatically have everything that goes along with being that person.

If you want to be a rich and powerful person, you need to BE a powerful person who attracts and controls lots of money. You have to SEE YOURSELF as that RICH AND POWERFUL PERSON. You have to visualize the way the Rich and Powerful You will be behaving. How "THAT you" will be speaking, interacting with people, exerting self-control and discipline... In short, you need to visualize every possible aspect that you can about the way you want your life to BE.

Margo Anand suggests – and I find this to be enormously helpful as a shorthand for Sex Magic ceremonies – that you create your visualization of what you're trying to manifest, and then you assign to that visualization a unique SYMBOL to represent everything that you're trying to manifest.

Remember, it's up to YOU to CREATE your OWN MAGIC POWERS.

No one can do it for you.

If you want to harness the power that resides inside every human being, and to bend that power to your own designs, you are the only person who is going to be able to figure out what is necessary for you to be able to use that magic power.

You have to be like Spiderman, and experience the path of figuring out your own personal spider-web creation techniques.

For the sake of providing you whatever insight you may gain from this, here's my account of how I was able to discover my own magical power.

Cheryl and I got back from *Spiderman*, and she agreed to join me in the ceremony.

We each selected a robe (from our collection of the many white cotton robes we've brought back from spas around the globe) and designated our respective Ceremonial Robe.

Then I prepared altars in key locations around the property and within the house.

Magic ceremonies often begin by creating a protective circle in which to perform the ceremonies. In order to describe the protective circle, I designated four markers as anchors of the four directions of the circle, including the swimming pool at the north, a wooden ceremonial altar she'd brought back from Thailand at the east, a rock altar I'd constructed with stones collected from around her property at the south, and the koi pond I had built for her birthday on the east side of the property.

We began at the north point of the circle, lighting candles that we set adrift in the water, then firing up a bunch of tied sage. Standing at the edge of the swimming pool in our robes at exactly midnight, I raised one hand to the heavens and pointed my other hand at the water, saying, "I am the magician Clint Arthur, and I call upon the powers of the North and the North Star to protect this circle. I am drawing that power down through me, and am depositing that power in this body of water, to designate the northern edge of our protective circle."

Despite the fact that it was a warm Los Angeles night in the month of June, while I spoke my incantations, I was amazed to see smoke coming out of my mouth with every breath and syllable. I was also pleasantly surprised to see a halo of energy surrounding the arm and hand that I held upraised to the heavens.

Cheryl spoke words to the same effect at the northern point, and then we moved to each of the other three markers around the circle, repeating similar incantations.

Then we moved inside with the sage and lit candles on an altar we constructed in the bedroom. On the mantle above her fireplace sits a Thai Buddha sculpture. In each of the Buddha's hands we placed a number of coins until the total came to nine. In the Buddha's lap we also placed crystals and rocks we'd collected during our travels. Finally we saged the bed and lit candles and incense on the night table at the head of the bed.

Then we removed our robes and got naked on the bed.

Cheryl is a big gorgeous blonde, and at that moment I recognized her to be exactly the woman that I've been looking for all my life.

We each knelt on the bed, facing each other, and as I looked into her eyes, I said, "The highest in me honors the highest in you. Namaste."

She repeated that back to me, and I felt us transcend to a new level that I had never felt with her before. Something more profound. Something more powerful.

We hugged with a heart-to-heart hug, which lasted a long time. During our hug I began to feel our heartbeats synchronizing, and the rate of our breathing coming into harmony.

I asked her to sit in my lap, in yab yum, and we exchanged the breath of the Goddess, one breathing in while the other breathed out, in rhythm and connection for many minutes.

Then I said, "Visualize the change you want to create in your life, and see that change taking place in your mind's eye as we continue to breath the Breath of the Goddess."

We both visualized the people who we wanted to become...

Saw ourselves – in our mind's eye – being the person who we wanted ourselves to be...

I saw myself walking the way That Man walked...

Talking the way That Man talked...

Holding myself erect with the posture of the rich and powerful man I would BE, and that I was BECOMING...

FEELING THE GREAT FEELING that was each moment of life lived by That Future Version of Myself...

Enjoying the personal power and self-worth That Man enjoys...

As fully as I could, I was moving out of my own current self and my current existence, and I was BEING That Man that I was becoming...

All the while Cheryl was having her own experience of Becoming...

And we were circulating magic-charged breaths and sympathetic intentions.

We did that for a long time, and then I said, "You are going to see in your mind's eye a symbol that represents everything that you want yourself to become. When that symbol enters your mind, you will transfer all the attributes of change that you want for yourself into that symbol, and see those changes come to reality in conjunction with that symbol."

Sharing more Goddess Breath, we continued in yab yum as we each visualized our symbol and our future self demonstrating the attributes we wanted to manifest.

I saw myself driving on the freeways with a new, easy calm and assurance, talking on my cell phone in a relaxed and powerful manner...

And I blended the image of my symbol – the American flag – with those attitudes and mannerisms...

I could see my posture as more erect and, at the same time, more relaxed...

I could hear a new strength in my voice, sounding deep and knowing and full of ease...

I felt a new level of profound self-confidence, and I felt the power of that inner fortitude glowing inside me while I drove, and everywhere I looked there were American flags representing this transformation.

After we did that for a long time, I said, "What is your symbol?"

She said, "The sun."

I said, "Okay, your desires are symbolized by the sun. Now I want you to lie face down on the bed, and visualize the sun in your base chakra."

She lay down on top of the cotton sheet, and I sat beside her and cupped my hand between her yoni and her anus...

Letting her feel the warmth of my flesh at her base chakra...

I said, "Visualize the sun at your base."

Then I bent over her base chakra and began toning the sound "Ahhhhhh."

And all the time that I toned, I visualized the sun in my mind's eye.

After a while I moved my body between her legs and continued to breathe on and tone over her base chakra.

Then I moved my hands over her second chakra, above her navel, and said, "Now visualize the sun in your stomach, and feel the presence of this power in your second chakra."

While she lay there visualizing, I put my hands over the base of her spine, and I knelt down to put my mouth over my hands and tone the sound "Ahhhhhhh" over the base of her spine, all the while visualizing the sun.

Then I moved up to the place above her solar plexus and repeated the process, with my tones increasing in frequency and power...

Moving up to the heart chakra...

The throat chakra...

The third eye...

Up to her crown chakra...

And finally, sending out her symbol on the ASTRAL PLANE...

Visualizing the rays of Cheryl's sun shining bright into the all-powerful network of the collective consciousness and universal subconscious mind...

Beaming the symbol of her changes, the symbol of who she was becoming...

Harmonizing and echoing and reinforcing the power of her visualization with my own.

It was SO INTENSE...

The vibrations...

The energy...

The connection...

The power.

Then I vocally led her back down through her crown, to her throat, into her heart, solar plexus, stomach, and finally the base chakra, to reground her in her own body.

At each point I sent my energy to her through my hands...

Knowing that by holding my hands over each chakra with the intention of sending her the energy, it was indeed happening.

When that was over, I let her lie there for a while; then I instructed her to slowly sit up when she was ready.

Then it was my turn.

I lay face-down on the bed, and we both began to visualize my symbol, the American flag.

As she sent energy to each of my chakras, she started saying words that I found to be very nurturing and supportive.

Neither of us knew where the words were coming from; they were flowing through her in a free-form magical spell, and I was loving it.

She said, "Visualize the American flag waving over you as you stand there in all your strength and glory...

"Symbolizing everything that you want to become...

"All the strength and wisdom inside you...

"All the power and courage you could ever want or ever need, flowing through you and emanating from you, and symbolized by the American flag.

"Feel that strength, and feel that power, living within you...

"Driving you...

"Guiding you...

"Fortifying you...

"Growing inside you...

"Giving you all the wisdom...

"Empowering you with everything you need...

"Everything you could ever want...

"Every desire is yours...

"Every wish...

"It's yours."

Bringing that experience through every energy point in my body, up from my base...

Through my stomach...

Into my solar plexus...

Heart...

Throat...

Third eye...

Into my crown...

And finally exploding my intentions out of my head and up into the Astral Plane!

WOOOOOOOOOOOOOOOOOOOOOOWWWWWWW
WWWWWWWWWWWWWWWWW!!!!!!!!!!

What a rush...

Such exhilaration...

To build that energy and send it out into the collective unconscious...

To create the vision and share it with the universal subconscious...

Phew!!!!!

Then she breathed hot breaths of love on each of my chakras, moving down from the crown, all the way to my base.

It took me several minutes of just lying there when the ceremony was over to feel like it had come to a conclusion.

When it did, I sat up and we hugged for a long time.

After that, we did one more ceremony, which has since become a very potent favorite of ours:

First I put one hand on her heart chakra...

And with the other hand I stimulate her Goddess spot...

All the while we are visualizing her symbol...

And especially at the point where she releases sacred amrita...

After that, once she has caught her breath and feels ready to focus on me and my symbol...

She gets on her hands and knees, I get on my knees, and she honors my lingam...

Giving me her uniquely capable loving lips and tongue and throat in support and harmonizing with my visualizations of my symbol...

All the while that she is honoring me with her love and thoughts, I visualize my symbol working its way up through my chakras, and at the moment of orgasm, I visualize an explosion of American flags shooting forth in every direction out onto the astral plane...

And in particular I try to vocalize the release of this energy with a gigantic "AHHHHHHHHHHHHHHH!!!!!!!!!!!!"

Often the sound comes out as a powerful ROAR…

The animal energy in me unable to be contained…

While she drinks in my creative force…

Giving me total acceptance…

The utmost feeling of love a man can know.

While the charge of orgasm leaves my body, I visualize bringing myself back down into my crown chakra, back down through the flute of energy, all the way to my sex center, then my base…

And to conclude the ceremony, we hold each other in an embrace of love and compassion, cuddling and integrating with each other's energy, until we both fall asleep…

My final recollections of the night being soft whispers of "Love, love, love, love…"

REVIEW QUIZ

1. Benevolent use of Sex Magic can have a _____ impact on one's own life and the destiny of humanity.

2. It's up to _____ to create your own magic powers.

3. Sex magic operates along the lines of visualization, only on a much _____ level.

4. Humans move toward _____ and away from _____.

5. Sex magic can be _____ effective at manifesting changes in personality or character traits.

6. Use a _____ as "shorthand" for your goals or desired outcome from Sex Magic rituals.

7. Use all the sexual techniques in this book to _____ your Sex Magic experiences.

8. True or false: You can do Sex Magic alone or with a partner.

9. The key to the entire process of Sex Magic is ____.

9
NON-EJACULATORY SEX

RELEASE

Suzy was the first Goddess I ever met who believed that men should "release."

Goddess Natalia and Dr. Clarke and many others often spoke of "the little death" that accompanied every male ejaculation.

I had been told stories – legends really – of the great Indian tantra masters who hardly ever ejaculated. I asked Michael the Red about it the day after the puja, and he told me, "I've met men who practiced ejaculation control in India. They might ejaculate only once a year, and then it would only be during a sacred ritual or ceremony. Those men looked like they were thirty years old – they had that much energy and power saved up from conserving their seed.

"There was a time," Michael the Red confided, "when I didn't come for more than a year. I knew all these Goddesses around town, women in the tantra community, and they would all want to have sex with me, trying to get me to cum. It was like a competition. They were trying everything they could do, every trick they knew, to get me to cum, but I just wouldn't do it. I wouldn't let go of my seed, my energy, no matter what they did."

I said, "Wow."

He said, "That was a very powerful time in my life. I would have orgasm after orgasm after orgasm, but they were all internal orgasms. And all that energy was circulating within me. And when I finally did let go, it was at a ceremony in Maui, and it was unbelievable."

THE ACT vs. THE FACT

Many times, guys are more concerned with the FACT that they are having sex than they are with the actual sex ACT itself.

That's why, when I get a lot of letters and emails addressed to the New Sex Advisor about lack of staying power, the answer is really pretty simple:

THE KEY TO EXTENDED STAYING POWER

Take pleasure in HER pleasure...

Focus on her eyes...

Feel how soft her skin feels against yours...

Feel your own strength in your muscles...

Forget about cumming – focus on loving...

And be sure to masturbate sometime earlier in the day prior to an evening encounter.

Also, as mentioned earlier, the ancient Asian technique of counting strokes is another great way to increase sexual staying power. Manifest your INTENTION by using your ATTENTION.

It's one thing to say, "We made love for ten or twelve minutes." It's another thing to say, "I gave her 999 long strokes and 450 short strokes." When you get to the point where you know exactly how many strokes you're doing, you will find that your mastery, control, and sexual power will be at an expert level.

NEW SENSUAL SALES POWER

A few weeks after our very first experiences with Sex Magic, Cheryl and I flew to Las Vegas and checked into the Venetian Hotel.

For the afternoon of Friday, July 13, 2002, I scheduled appointments with five of the top restaurants in one of the top restaurant cities in America.

That morning we each enjoyed an eighty-minute massage at the Canyon Ranch Spa. Then we met up in our suite, and just before I left for my first appointment, I had her get naked on her knees and honor me with some powerful, loving deep throat.

I got fully erect and grooved with the sensations of my penis clicking into her throat…

And once my sexual energy was fully activated, I zipped my erection into my pants, kissed her goodbye, thanked her, and went off to conquer the culinary pinnacles of Picasso, Renoir, Lutece, Charlie Palmer's and the Prime Steakhouse.

Within ten days of that trip, all five of the chefs that I met with had become customers of my business, the Five Star Butter Co.

I had used all the lessons and knowledge you have learned in this book, and had proven their effectiveness beyond a shadow of a doubt.

Now the power is sitting clearly before you in your mind's eye.

You have only to begin practicing what you already know…

You have only to access the inner reservoir of nature's most potent energy and force…

Your God-given power to create and manifest every dream.

The Nine Free Secrets of New Sensual Power are yours to enjoy for the betterment of your life, and the lives of your loved ones, of your family, and of the entire world.

Namaste.

THOUGHTS ABOUT LOVE

Be careful!

You are now an extremely dangerous entity.

You possess more knowledge about sexual power and mastery than most people will ever learn in their entire lifetime.

G-spot sex in itself is SO POTENT that it can "fool" people into believing they're in love with each other even if they've just met and don't even KNOW each other.

On top of that you have all the information about male multiple orgasms, anal sex, aural sex, oral sex, sex magic, and non-ejaculatory sex at your command too.

It is safe to say that if you put these techniques into practice, anyone you have sex with could easily become your sexual slave or even your love slave.

They won't know what hit 'em!

Use this power wisely.

It's not always great to have *everyone* fall in love with you.

But it's AWESOME to have all this available to you for use in building a bond of love and intimacy with the One you want.

Always remember: Sexual power is the most potent force on earth. It can kill. And it can even revive the dead.

New Sex Advisor #35 © 2001 Clint Arthur & www.NewSex.org
New Sex Revives Dead Female Hollywood Executive

She hasn't let the L-word out of her mouth other than to say that she loves my cock…

She loves the way I fuck her…

She loves the way we feel…

She loves how I fill her up, so deep inside…

But not that she loves me.

A week ago we were in New Orleans, partying and bootlegging music at Jazz Fest.

Popping into a voodoo shop on Bourbon Street, I ask the man behind the counter for a love potion.

"You want a love potion?" he says calculatingly. Then he points to a short, trim black man with a graying beard and red vein-streaked eyes, a guy just seemingly hanging out in the middle of the store.

We step over to the little man and I ask, "You got a love potion?"

"Do I got a love potion?!" he chirps brightly. "Come with me!"

He drags us both by the arms out onto the street and around to the front window of the store.

"Look at that picture!" he says and points at a 5-by-7 color photo plastered onto the window pane.

A picture of him…

In some kind of African tribal costume…

And written in blood-red nail polish across the top of the photo, the headline "Modaddy, Prince of Love."

My eyes bug wide as I read the words aloud, then look at Cheryl for her reaction.

"Oh my God!" I exclaim in shock. "It's the Prince of Love! I found the Prince of Love!"

"Holy God!" Cheryl breathes, the words escaping her hidden consciousness…

Modaddy's eyes flick between our faces wild and charged with electricity of Bourbon Street night as I inspect his features for authenticity – and see it there pure.

"You want a love potion, man?" he says with a big cracked yellowing grin. "I got your love potion. I got love potion number 9!"

[Continued tomorrow]

Have YOU tried New Sex™?

New Sex Advisor #36 © 2001 Clint Arthur &www.NewSex.org
New Sex Revives Dead Female Hollywood Executive (Part 2)

The screams and loud live music of Bourbon Street all fade away into the background as Modaddy, the Prince of Love, produces out of his pocket a tiny brown vial of dark, cloudy herb-tinted oil.

A torn and soiled label on the container identifies its contents as "Love ... #9"

He slowly shakes the bottle before our eyes...

Cheryl digs her fingernails into my waist...

Again, our eyes totally bug with disbelief...

Is this really happening?

How serendipitous can life actually be?

"This is the real love potion, man..." he says with all confidence and joy. "You put this on your woman – it's guaranteed you gonna be doing some hot fucking."

"We're already doin' that!" I told him. "I want her to fall in love with me!"

"Oh, that's for sure, man," he laughs. Then he turns his eyes away from mine and takes in Cheryl's amazingly sexy curves and beautiful face.

"Dude," he says, "you are one lucky man."

"I know! I want this woman to be in love with me."

"Oh, she gonna be in love. This potion do the trick fo' sho'."

"How much?" I ask him.

"Yeah, how much?" Cheryl chimes in, with just the slightest anxiety in her voice.

"Usually I gets twenty dollars, man – make me an offer."

I peel a picture of Alexander Hamilton off my wad of cash and hand it over, not wanting to haggle over something so important with someone so special.

"Now what?" I ask, appraising the mysterious dark concoction in my palm.

"Put a drop on her left wrist," Modaddy says as he pockets his loot. "Then rub your right wrist on it till it feels hot."

"That's it?"

Modaddy steals a quick peck on Cheryl's cheek, then says, "That's it, brutha."

I twist off the cap and feel a crusty grit give way as it loosens.

Then I rub a dot of the lavender-scented oil onto her wrist and press against it with mine, per the instructions of New Orleans' Prince of Love…

Then I kiss Cheryl on the lips…

Her mouth and tongue and soul yield to my own…

And when we come up from the kiss and look around, the intoxicated din of revelry throbs in our ears…

And Modaddy is gone!

[Continued tomorrow]

Have YOU tried New Sex™?

New Sex Advisor #37 © 2001 Clint Arthur
New Sex Revives Dead Female Hollywood Executive (Part 3)

Last night she finally said it.

We had crawled into her big luxurious bed at one minute past midnight…

I was totally exhausted after a huge day.

Woke up around eleven, immediately started making love in the v-berth on my boat.

Her body so receptive and healthy, plush with sexual availability to me…

Pumping into her with my forearms and hands under her back, supporting and gripping her shoulders…

Positioning her torso and hips to the perfect angle…

Her legs yield wide open to me…

My naked hardness frictions against her naked interior vault…

Her head lolls on the pillow, ecstatic from our perfect connection...

The moment so hot and sexy and NATURAL to me that I feel my seed welling up from deep within...

So I pull out and splatter her stomach with a Rorschach of cum...

Her green-gray saucer eyes stare with loving desire and fulfillment, but she does not say anything about...

Love...

Seven days have passed since our encounter with Modaddy, the Prince of Love.

Her birthday had fallen on the Monday, and I gave her a LONG series of female ejaculations and G-spot orgasms using the New Sex™ techniques, step-by-step for guaranteed effectiveness...

Bringing her to peaks of puddling, cum-splashing ecstasy...

Just as I KNEW I would...

Because the New Sex™ Techniques work every time...

But still she refrained from saying IT.

In her house on Saturday I gave another huge series of ejaculations and New Sex™ passion, but still she held tight against any reference to the L-word.

Then, after an intense lovemaking session Sunday morn, we got dressed for the gym and I put a dot of Modaddy's secret formula on her right wrist, then rubbed it with my left wrist until it got hot.

"What if a woman puts the potion on a man's right wrist?" she asked me, quite the little joker.

I said, "Don't mess with voodoo."

We had a good gym workout, then went back to my boat, lunched on raw oysters and steak with raw goat cheese and Perrier. Then I worked on my engine and got it to start again after too many months lying dormant, and we moved my boat and entire life from my old marina to the new one.

My legs were SORE.

She massaged them during dinner, which, as usual, we ate seated on the floor in the living room of her home…

Raw beef and lamb and mussels with goat and Manchego cheeses, fresh basil, olive oil, and two varieties of imported olives…

Cold Pinot Grigio…

Then we went to bed and as we cuddled, she batted her long beautiful eyelashes. I saw her make a mental decision to stop fighting against it…

The potion and the techniques are much too strong…

Even for her…

The tough, battle-scarred, heart-hardened Hollywood executive…

Looking into my eyes as we hold each other's naked bodies, she softly speaks those words I've been so longing to hear:

"You know I am in love with you."

[Tomorrow, the Conclusion]

New Sex Advisor #38 © 2001 Clint Arthur & www.NewSex.org
New Sex Revives Dead Female Hollywood Executive (Conclusion)

At 6:57 a.m. I awake from a dream in which I've been elected U.S. Senator for the state of California. I was smoking a joint in my office in the Capitol building, casually informing people that I'd been elected – because nobody knew…

Next thing I know the dream is gone, and lying naked beside me in her big fluffy bed, my tan, curvy, sweetie-pie – the luxuriant and ever-receptive Cheryl…

I look at her sleeping there, and I know that she is completely available to me…

Her total willingness to yield and open herself for me…

Is like a drug – Viagra.

I spy a small piece of a white plastic bag stuck to her shoulder, and as I gently remove it she stirs from slumber and looks at me...

Those big green tigress eyes somehow sharp and alert even fresh from REM...

Playfully, she says, "What?"

I just dive down under the covers, between her legs...

Her thighs spread to allow access...

Breathing hot breaths, my mouth an inch from the close-trimmed hairs of her love zone...

Just breathing and breathing...

I kiss her there, tenderly with my lips and tongue...

Soon she shifts her body so that she lies beneath me with her mouth in position to do to me what she does so exquisitely.

In moments she is also kissing my sex...

And it fills with blood and passion-energy so quick from her expert nibbles and licks...

Sucking me into her throat...

The base of my shaft...

Such authority...

It makes me delirious!

Soon I am too big for her to deep throat...

We rotate for insertion...

And my raging hardness fills her...

I can feel that my penis is bigger...

Desire is the inspiration for growth and edge-cut throbs...

Her walls so soft and wet and warm...

Our lovemaking, as usual, so full of passion...

Especially when we dog...

SO dripping wet.

After, we cuddle and I keep staring into her eyes because I can't even believe how lucky I am to have such a sweet, wonderful, passionate, sexual, sensual, loving, good-hearted woman in my life...

To be in love with her...

Together with her...

"What are you thinking about?" she asks.

It's so totally quiet – only the sounds of our breathing, a bird chirping in her garden...

I'm stroking her left temple, just at the base of her golden hairline...

I whisper, "How sweet this moment is."

She takes one breath, then another, and then one more...

Then she says, "You brought me back to life. For so many years I was just dead inside."

Have YOU tried New Sex™ ?

<u>REVIEW QUIZ</u>

1. Men are often more impressed by the _____ that they
    are having sex than they are by the actual sex ___.

2. Ejaculation control is about preservation of _____.

3. List five methods for extending male "staying power."

4. New Sensual Sales Power operates on the basis of
    activating _____ energy.

5. Residing within everyone is an _____ _____ of
    nature's most potent energy and force.

6. The Nine Free Secrets of New Sensual Power can be used
    by you on an _____ basis.

7. By using your New Sensual Power, you can better
    _____ life, that of your _____ _____, and the entire
    _____.

8. G-spot sex can make strangers believe they are in
    _____.

9. Only sexual power has the potency to _____ life.

NEW SEX INSTITUTE
CERTIFICATION

To apply for New Sex Institute certification as a Scholar of Advanced Lovemaking Techniques, compile the following:

1) Xerox Copies of all 9 quizzes in this book with your answers <u>clearly</u> written in the blank spaces.
2) A type-written essay (minimum 250 words) about your experiences using the techniques and systems detailed in this book.
3) A cover sheet which includes your name, age, address, and email address (if available.)
4) A check or money order payable to C.A.I. for $9.95 to cover processing and handling.

Mail all of the above in a 9" X 12" envelope to:
New Sex Institute, PO Box 11682, Marina del Rey, CA 90295

Tests with a correct score of 75% or above will receive a Certificate of Achievement.

Tests with a correct score of 85% or above will receive a Certificate of Excellence.

Tests with a correct score of 95% or above will receive certification as an Expert Sex Scholar Extraordinaire.

All certificates are suitable for framing and are personally signed by Clint Arthur.

All applications become the property of New Sex Institute. Under no circumstances will any materials be returned.

ABOUT THE AUTHOR

Clint Arthur founded the New Sex Institute in 1999 to help men and women create more intimacy and love in their lives using the power of sexual ecstasy.

He is a graduate of the University of Pennsylvania's Wharton School of Business, where he specialized in Entrepreneurship. He is also the President of Five Star Butter Co., exclusive distributor of the world's most expensive and best quality butter and cream, served by 9 of the top gourmet restaurants in America. His education and sales experience make him uniquely qualified to teach his Secrets of New Sensual Power to entrepreneurs, agents, and sales professionals through books, audio-visual programs, and seminars.

OTHER WORKS BY CLINT ARTHUR

Ultimate Female Orgasms
(Simon & Schuster, UK)
co-author with Tom Leonardi.

Save Your Marriage With Oral Sex
New Sex Institute E-book
Author

New Free Sex™ (VHS; DVD)
Step-by-step System for Super-Sensual Lovemaking
Producer, Presenter

New Sex Now (VHS; DVD)
Video Guide to Life's Ultimate Pleasure.
Producer, Presenter

Goddess Worship (VHS)
How to make any woman feel worshipped like a Goddess.
Producer, Worshipper.

Arte's Gay Tantra Sex Voyeur Experience (VHS)
Producer, Director

Master Sex Talk (Audio CD)
Producer, Performer

New Free Sex Oral (Audio CD)
Producer, Performer

WEBSITES
www.NewSex.org
www.NewSensualPower.com
www.IloveNewFreeSex.com
www.NewGaySex.com

NEW SEX NOW

The step-by-step video guide to New Sex™
will take you and your lover to
uncharted sexual and emotional territories.
In this tasteful erotic presentation for adults
you will *see* & *hear* everything you need
in order to *feel* life's ultimate pleasure.

I N C L U D E S
•New Sex™ Techniques
•Ultimate Female Orgasms™
•Ultimate Simultaneous Orgasms for Couples
•Exquisite Intimacy & Golden Afterglow
•Ultimate Erotic Massage™

Techniques taught on *New Sex Now*
enable ANY WOMAN to experience
G-Spot Orgasms, Female Ejaculation,
Sacred Orgasms & Simultaneous Ejaculations with her lover.

"One of our most worthwhile purchases this year!
We tried the techniques right away - they worked!
We were so surprised,we could hardly contain ourselves!"
-R. Seacord, MD

"I watched the video, and that night
my girlfriend didn't know what hit her!"
-Tom, age 34

"Words are inadequate for this. It is mind-blowingly incredible! The height of
excellence! Just do what you can to try this – it will change your life."
-Gabriel W., age 28

TO ORDER YOUR COPY OF *NEW SEX NOW (color; 58 minutes)*
Go to www.NewSex.org or
Send $38.95 (includes $4 s&h)
payable to "C. Arthur" PO Box 11682, Marina del Rey, CA 90295
Be sure to SPECIFY DVD or VHS, and include your shipping information!
All of our Programs feature a 100% Money Back Satisfaction Guarantee

GODDESS WORSHIP

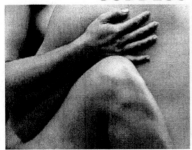

When I was looking for a woman to star in *New Sex Now* with me,
I became friends with a few of the magnificent tantra Goddesses
at www.GoddessTemple.com

And I became very curious about the ritual of Goddess Worship
that a number of those Goddesses offer to their clients.
It was my great fortune to have the opportunity to participate in
an actual Goddess Worship Ritual with the
gorgeous, sensuous, and gifted Goddess Lilith.
That experience was filmed and recorded for
the enlightenment of all who wish to learn
how make a woman feel worshipped like a goddess.

Directed by Dr. Corynna Clarke, one of the world's foremost
spokespersons on the subject of Sacred Sexuality, this easy-to-follow
practical guide transforms ancient wisdom into your own nightly ritual,
and features an hour of beautiful Goddess music by then 20 year-old
prodigy Jillian Speer. Shot in Full Color, 68 minutes.

I am proud to have produced this film, and offer a
100% money-back guarantee of your absolute satisfaction
and delight with the Goddess Worship experience.

Sincerely,
Clint "Arte" Arthur

"The best film of the genre!"
-Hyla Kass, Ph.D.

"Men, listen to the goddess --
Lilith is exquisite!"
-Charles Muir

TO ORDER YOUR COPY OF *GODDESS WORSHIP*
Go to www.NewSex.org
Or send $38.95 (includes $4 s&h) payable to
"C. Arthur" PO Box 11682, Marina del Rey, CA 90295
AVAILABLE in VHS ONLY. Be sure to include your shipping information.

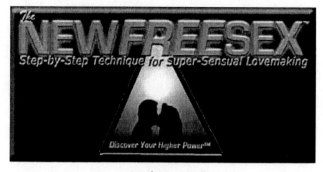

Volume 1
Her Ultimate Pleasure
The Pathway To God
Includes: Step-by-step G-Spot Orgasms, Female Ejaculation, Simultaneous Ejaculation, Ultimate Erotic Massage, & more.

Volume 2
His Ultimate Pleasure &
Advanced Lovemaking Techniques
Includes: Male Multiple Orgasms & Ejaculations, Toning, Erotic Sacrifice, & more.

This step-by-step program will guide you and your lover to un-dreamed-of realms of sensual pleasure.
Clint Arthur uses tasteful plain English to explain everything you need to know about his step-by-step system for maximizing a woman's pleasure, a man's pleasure, and a couple's pleasure together.

These techniques are guaranteed to enable your sexual euphoria each and every time you use them.

No special skills or aptitudes required.
Contains no nudity or foul language.
